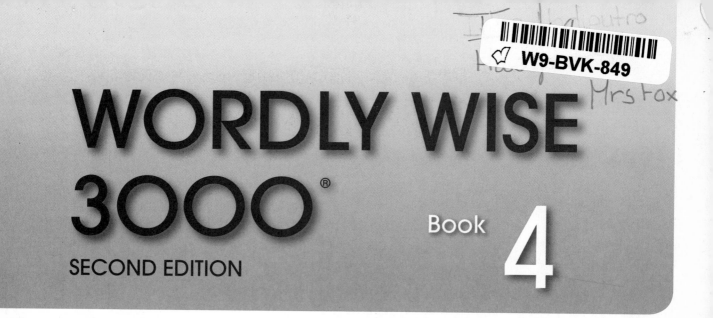

WORDLY WISE 3000®

SECOND EDITION

Book 4

Kenneth Hodkinson | Sandra Adams

EDUCATORS PUBLISHING SERVICE
Cambridge and Toronto

Original cover design: Hugh Price
Interior design: Sarah Cole
Acquisitions/Development: Kate Moltz
Editors: Wendy Drexler, Elissa Gershowitz, Stacey Nichols Kim, Theresa Trinder, Laura Woollett
Editorial Assistant: Becky Ticotsky
Senior Editorial Manager: Sheila Neylon

Printed in USA

ISBN 978-0-8388-2822-9

6 7 8 9 CRW 12 11 10 09 08

Contents

Lesson 1

Word List
Study the definitions of the words below; then do the exercises for the lesson.

benefit
be´ nə fit
①

v. To help or be helpful to; to be useful to.
That preschool program **benefits** young children.
n. 1. Something that is useful or helpful, that does good.
One of the **benefits** of my exercise program is that I sleep better.
2. An event held to raise money for a cause.
The library's **benefit** raised enough money for a new children's room.

complete
kəm plēt´
②

adj. 1. Having no missing parts; whole.
She bought a **complete** set of woodworking tools at a yard sale.
2. Finished.
The new wing on the high school is now **complete**.
v. To finish.
Schubert did not **complete** his eighth symphony, so it's nicknamed "The Unfinished."

develop
di vel´ əp
③

v. 1. To go through a process of growth.
Running regularly **develops** strong leg muscles.
2. To bring or come into being.
The day after I brushed against the poison ivy, a rash **developed** on my leg.
3. To apply chemicals to photographic film to bring out the picture.
I want to learn to **develop** my own pictures.

dismay
dis mā´
④

v. To cause feelings of fear, worry, or surprise.
A large crack in the ceiling of our newly painted kitchen **dismayed** my parents.
n. A sudden loss of courage because of fear or worry.
Just after we began hiking, we were filled with **dismay** when we heard the rumble of a rockslide.

ease
ēz
⑤

n. A state of being comfortable—without worry, pain, or trouble.
Since I took a course in public speaking, I feel much more at **ease** when I give a speech.
v. To make less worried, pained, or troubled.
It **eased** my mind to hear you were safe.

hail
hāl
⑥

n. Small lumps of frozen rain.
The **hail** bouncing off the metal roof of the garage made a terrible racket.
v. 1. To fall as frozen rain.
My father's corn plants suffered a lot of damage when it **hailed** yesterday.
2. To greet or welcome, usually with admiration.
The band played "**Hail** to the Chief" as the president came in.

lack
lak
⑦

v. To be without.
He never sees the funny side of things because he **lacks** a sense of humor.
n. A shortage.
A **lack** of money to pay the staff forced our library to close on weekends.

1

master
mas´ tər

⑦

adj. 1. Chief; main.
Throw the **master** switch to turn on the power.
2. Having or showing great skill.
Rick is a **master** carpenter.
v. To become skilled at.
My mother **mastered** the new computer program in just a few weeks.

patriot
pā´ trē ət

⑧

n. One who loves, supports, and is loyal to his or her country.
Giuseppe Garibaldi was an Italian **patriot** who fought tirelessly to unite his country.
patriotic (pā trē ä´ tik) *adj.* Having or showing love of one's country.
"America the Beautiful" is a **patriotic** song that was written by Katherine Lee Bates.
patriotism *n.* Love of one's country.
Some people show their **patriotism** by proudly flying their country's flag.

project
prä´ jekt

⑨

n. A plan or idea for doing something.
My science **project** is going to show what acid rain does to plants.
v. (prə jekt´) 1. To stick out.
Nails are still **projecting** out of the new floor, so be careful where you walk.
2. To cause an image to be shown on a screen.
This machine **projects** color slides but not movies.

recommend
rə kə mend´

10

v. 1. To make a statement of praise.
I loved *The Secret Garden* and I highly **recommend** it.
2. To give advice; to suggest.
Dentists usually **recommend** that you have a checkup twice a year.

remark
ri märk´

11

v. To say; to make a comment.
My grandmother **remarked** on how well I looked.
n. Something said; a comment.
When no one else could think of anything to say, I made a **remark** about how badly we needed rain.
remarkable *adj.* Deserving of being noticed; unusual.
For such a young child, he had **remarkable** strength.

represent
re pri zent´

v. 1. To stand for or in place of.
Three dots **represent** the letter "S" in the Morse code.
2. To act in place of.
Each state in the U.S. elects two senators to **represent** it in Congress.

sufficient
sə fish´ ənt

adj. Enough to fill a need.
Ten lessons on the oboe were **sufficient** to earn me a place in the school band.

utter
u´ tər

v. To make sounds with the voice; to speak.
Please don't **utter** another word.

1A Finding Meanings

Choose two phrases to form a sentence that correctly uses a word from Word List 1. Write each sentence in the space provided.

1. (a) a useful aid.   (c) Dismay is
   (b) Hail is   (d) frozen rain.

Hail is frozen rain.

2. (a) A remarkable plan is   (c) one that will probably fail.
   (b) the main one.   (d) A master plan is

A master plan is the main one.

3. (a) a place to relax.   (c) A benefit is
   (b) an event that raises money. (d) A patriot is

A benefit is an event that raises money.

4. (a) A complete picture is one that is   (c) very unusual.
   (b) A remarkable picture is one that is   (d) not easy to see.

A remarkable picture is one that is very unusual.

5. (a) to bring it to an end.   (c) to make it grow.
   (b) To develop something is   (d) To ease something is

To develop something is to make it grow.

6. (a) to control it.   (c) To utter something is
   (b) To complete something is   (d) to say it.

To utter something is to say it.

7. (a) stand in for him or her.   (c) To represent someone is to
   (b) invite him or her.   (d) To recommend someone is to

To represtand someone is to stand in for him or her.

8. (a) To lack food   (c) is to have more than enough.
   (b) To have sufficient food   (d) is to have enough.

To have sufficient food is to have enough.

9. (a) to show it on a screen.   (c) To recommend a picture is
   (b) to change it slightly.   (d) To project a picture is

To project a picture is to show it on a screen.

1B Just the Right Word

Improve each of the following sentences by crossing out the bold phrase and replacing it with a word (or a form of the word) from Word List 1.

1. I sensed a ~~total absence~~ *lack* of enthusiasm when I suggested that we climb Mount Monadnock.

2. Martha Graham ~~brought into being~~ *developed* a new style of dance in America.

3. The bookshelf ~~sticks out~~ *projects* too far into the room and has to be made narrower.

4. I took a hot bath to help to ~~take away the pain in~~ *ease* my aching muscles.

5. Olga Ramirez expects her novel to be ~~at a point where no further work is necessary~~ *completed* by the end of the week.

6. My uncle ~~became very skilled at speaking~~ *mastered* French after spending a year in France.

7. In English, the letter "c" ~~stands for~~ *reprenets* two different sounds.

8. Young children ~~are helped~~ *benefit* a great deal from being read to every day.

9. The article ended with a reminder that there is more to showing ~~love of one's country~~ *patriotism* than flying your country's flag.

10. The news that the last train had just left ~~worried and distressed~~ *dismayed* us.

11. The track coach ~~gave me the suggestion~~ *recommended* that I warm up before starting my run.

benefit
complete
develop
dismay
ease
hail
lack
master
patriot
project
recommend
remark
represent
sufficient
utter

1C Applying Meanings

Circle the letter of each correct answer to the questions below. A question may have <u>more</u> than one correct answer.

1. Which of the following might fill someone with **dismay**?

    (a) losing ten dollars

    (b) finding ten dollars

    (c) finding a staple in a tuna sandwich

    (d) finding celery in a tuna sandwich

2. Which of the following might put someone at **ease**?

    (a) a friendly smile

    (b) a "Keep Out" sign

    (c) a warm welcome

    (d) a promise to help

3. Which of the following might be **hailed** by people?

   (a) a train crash

   (b) a cure for a disease

   (c) a popular president

   (d) rain after a long dry spell

4. Which of the following is a **complete** sentence and needs a period?

   (a) I'm cold.

   (b) Let's go.

   (c) The bus for Toledo

   (d) My hockey puck

5. A rich person could **lack** which of the following?

   (a) money

   (b) freedom

   (c) time

   (d) good health

6. Which of the following could mean a person is **patriotic**?

   (a) making money

   (b) having a hobby

   (c) voting in elections

   (d) serving one's country

7. Which of the following is a **remark**?

   (a) You look tired.

   (b) 2 + 2 = 4

   (c) What on earth are you doing?

   (d) A B C D

8. Which of the following **represent** other people?

   (a) state senators

   (b) taxi drivers

   (c) storekeepers

   (d) lawyers

1D Word Study

Synonyms are words that have the same or similar meaning. *Big* and *large* are synonyms. Both words have to do with great size.

Look at the words below. Circle the two words that are synonyms in each group of four.

1. harm	hail	benefit	help
2. rush	finish	complete	lack
3. dismay	develop	grow	need
4. alarm	joy	hunger	dismay
5. ease	growth	comfort	project
6. remark	hail	forget	greet
7. shortage	lack	promise	return
8. suggest	satisfy	recommend	promise
9. comment	remark	disturbance	pause
10. repeat	utter	represent	say

1E Passage

Read the passage below; then complete the exercise that follows.

Sequoya's Gift

Sequoya was a **remarkable** man in many ways. He was a skilled silversmith and painter and had also served as a soldier. But he is remembered today for inventing a written language.

Sequoya was a member of the Cherokee nation, the son of a Native American mother and a British father. A **patriotic** person, he was **dismayed** that white people were taking over more and more of the Cherokee lands.

There was no easy way for Cherokees to be in touch with each other because they **lacked** a written language. Words spoken in Cherokee were lost as soon as they were **uttered**. Sequoya believed that the Cherokee people would **benefit** greatly if they had a written language and could read and write. Then newspapers could spread the word of what was happening to people, and books could record their history. He made up his mind that he would try to **develop** a written language for his people.

The **project**, which he began in 1809, took twelve years to **complete**. He and his daughter worked together. She carefully sounded out each syllable, and Sequoya **represented** it with a letter that he chose from the English, Greek, and Hebrew alphabets. Eighty-six letters were **sufficient** to cover all the sounds of the Cherokee language.

Sequoya used this new written language in a message he sent to the leaders of the Cherokee nation. The leaders were impressed with how simple the system was, and they **recommended** that the new written language be taught to everyone who wanted to learn to read and write. People liked it because it could be learned quickly and with **ease**, and those who **mastered** it went on to teach others. The Cherokees set up schools to teach Sequoya's alphabet and began to publish books and newspapers in their new language. The first Native American newspaper, the *Cherokee Phoenix*, was published on February 21, 1828. It was followed by a flood of other newspapers and books.

In his later years, Sequoya travelled throughout North America studying other Native American languages. Everywhere he went he was **hailed** for his invention, which played such an important part in uniting the Cherokee people. He died in 1843. His memory is honored in California's giant sequoia trees, and its beautiful Sequoia National Park.

benefit

complete

develop

dismay

ease

hail

lack

master

patriot

project

recommend

remark

represent

sufficient

utter

Answer each of the following questions in the form of a <u>sentence</u>. If a question does not contain a vocabulary word from this lesson's word list, use one in your answer. Use each word only once. Questions and answers will then contain all <u>fifteen words</u> (or forms of the words).

1. How can we tell that Sequoya was **patriotic**?

He was upset white men were talking away there land.

2. What is the meaning of **utter** as used in the passage?

To utter means to speak.

3. Why weren't any books written in Cherokee before 1821?

They lacked a written language.

4. How did Sequoya feel about what the white settlers were doing?

He felt dismayed!

5. What is the meaning of **develop** as it is used in the passage?

Developed means to bring or come.

6. How did Sequoya use the English, Greek, and Hebrew alphabets?

He represented each sound from a letter from these alphabet.

7. Our alphabet has twenty-six letters. Why wasn't that number **sufficient** for the Cherokee alphabet?

The Cherokee language has more than 26 sounds so far 26 isn't enough

8. How long did Sequoya's work take?

It took twelve years clompete.

9. Did Sequoya work on his **project** alone or did he have help?

He worked on the project with his daughter.

10. Why was the new language popular with the people?

and with ease
It could be learned quickly and those who mastered went to teach others.

11. How can we tell that the Cherokee leaders liked the new system?

The leaders were immpressed and they recommended the new written language to be taught!

12. What is the meaning of **hailed** as it is used in the passage?

The meaning of hailed that is used in the passage means to greet.

13. How did the Cherokees help each other learn the new language?

When someone mastered the written language they taught others.

14. What was **remarkable** about Sequoya?

He was skilled as a silversmith, painter and also a soldier.

15. How does a written language **benefit** friends living far apart?

Newspapers would spread the word of what's happening.

FUN & FASCINATING FACTS

The Latin *bene* means "good" or "well" and forms a root of the word **benefit**. A *benefit* is something that is good for a person. Other words formed from this root include *benevolent*, which means "having a wish to do good" and *beneficial*, which means "doing good; being of help."

Some people (the Germans, for example) think of their country as a father and call it the fatherland; in fact, the word **patriot** comes from the Latin *pater*, which means "father." People of other countries, including Americans, think of their country not as the fatherland but as the motherland. If English had used the Latin for mother, which is *mater*, instead of the word for father, what would we call a person with a deep love of country?

In addition to its meaning as a verb, **utter** is also an adjective and means "total" or "absolute." (When the cellar door slammed shut behind us, we were left in *utter* darkness.); (I felt like an *utter* fool when the bike I had reported stolen was found just where I left it.)

Hale is an adjective that means "in good health." **Hail** and *hale* are homophones, words that sound alike but have different meanings and spellings.

Lesson 2

Word List
Study the definitions of the words below; then do the exercises for the lesson.

affect
ə fekt´

v. 1. To bring about a change in.
Do you think changing schools will **affect** my grades?
2. To pretend to be or to have.
The reporter **affected** an interest in buying a used car in order to get the salesperson to talk to her.

calculate
kal´ kyōō lāt

v. 1. To find the answer by using arithmetic.
I gave my sister the check so she could **calculate** her share of the bill.
2. To figure out by reasoning.
You'd better **calculate** the risks carefully before going on a long trip with that old car.

climate
klī´ mət

n. The average weather conditions of an area.
Florida's warm **climate** is perfect for growing oranges.

column
kä´ ləm

n. 1. A row of figures or words running down a printed page; anything arranged like that.
Do all the problems in the first **column** on page 30.
2. A tall, usually stone support that holds up something.
Forty-six marble **columns** support the roof of the Parthenon in Athens.
3. A regular newspaper or magazine article usually written by the same person.
My mother writes a weekly sports **column** for the *News-Tribune*.

decay
dē kā´

v. To rot.
Leaves left on the ground will **decay** over the winter.
n. A breaking down or rotting.
Dentists say tooth **decay** can be prevented by regular brushing and flossing.

exceed
ek sēd´

v. 1. To be more than.
The final score of Monday's game **exceeded** our best hopes.
2. To go beyond what is allowed.
The officer who stopped me told me never to **exceed** the speed limit again.
excess (ek ses´) *n.* More than enough; an extra amount.
Use what you need, and save the **excess**.
excessive *adj.* Too much or too great.
Last winter my parents paid an **excessive** amount for heating oil.

forbid
fər bid´

v. To order not to do something.
A state law **forbids** smoking in hospitals.
forbidden *adj.* Not allowed.
Eating in class is **forbidden**.

grove
grōv

n. A group of trees growing together with open space between them.
The children walked hand in hand through the **grove** of lemon trees.

limb
lim

n. 1. An arm, leg, or wing.
Bats use their webbed front and back **limbs** to fly.
2. A large tree branch.
The owl was perched on the top **limb** of the tree.

mammoth
ma´ məth

adj. Very large; huge.
The **mammoth** Seattle Skydome holds over fifty thousand people.

mature
mə choŏr´

v. To become fully grown or developed.
Rabbits **mature** in about six months and are then able to bear young.
adj. Fully grown or developed; adult.
My brother looks very **mature** for only eleven.

permit
pər mit´

v. To allow.
Some towns **permit** overnight parking downtown.
n. (pʉr´ mit) A written notice that allows a person to do something.
You need a **permit** to go fishing in that lake.

resist
ri zist´

v. 1. To refuse to give in to; to withstand.
Some kinds of corn **resist** disease better than others.
2. To work or fight against.
The armies of Genghis Khan were so powerful, it was useless to **resist** them.

scorch
skôrch

v. To burn slightly.
If you press a shirt with an iron that is too hot, you might **scorch** the cloth.
scorching *adj.* Very hot.
On such a **scorching** July day, the only thing I wanted after work was a swim in the ocean.

tower
tou´ ər

v. To stand above or higher than what is around it.
The Statue of Liberty **towers** above New York Harbor.
towering *adj.* Very high; tall.
Looking up at the **towering** skyscrapers gave me a stiff neck.

2A Finding Meanings

Choose two phrases to form a sentence that correctly uses a word from Word List 2. Write each sentence in the space provided.

1. (a) keep people out of a building.
   (b) support part of a building.
   (c) A column is used to
   (d) A permit is used to

A colum is used to support part of a building.

2. (a) A maple grove is
   (b) what is left after it is cut down.
   (c) A maple limb is
   (d) a large branch.

A maple limb is a large branch.

3. (a) A mammoth parade is   (c) one held once a year.
   (b) A forbidden parade is   (d) one that is very large.

A mammoth parade is one that is very large.

4. (a) To scorch something is to   (c) look closely into it.
   (b) To permit something is to   (d) allow it.

To permit something is to allow it.

5. (a) A climate is   (c) a group of paintings.
   (b) a group of trees.   (d) A grove is

A grove is a group of trees.

6. (a) To calculate something is to (c) To affect something is to
   (b) figure it out by reasoning.   (d) be against it.

To calculate something is to figure it out by reasoning.

7. (a) If something towers,   (c) it is starting to grow.
   (b) If something decays,   (d) it stands above what is around it.

If something towers it is starting to grow.

8. (a) to go beyond it.   (c) To exceed something is
   (b) To forbid something is   (d) to go back to it.

To exceed something is to go beyond.

9. (a) To resist something is   (c) to cause a change in it.
   (b) To affect something is   (d) to forget about it.

To affect something is to cause a change in it.

10. (a) an extra amount.   (c) a shortage.
    (b) A climate is   (d) An excess is

An excess is an extra amount.

2B Just the Right Word

Improve each of the following sentences by crossing out the bold phrase and replacing it with a word (or a form of the word) from Word List 2.

−2

80

1. Pat's **regular newspaper article** _column_ on gardening is very popular with readers.

2. Unfortunately, the cost of those sneakers **is more than** _exceeds_ what I've saved so far.

3. I tried to **figure out** _calcuate_ how much gas we would use on our trip to Nevada.

4. She **pretended to have** _affected_ a Southern accent, even though she was from New England.

5. Young people **develop into adults** much earlier than they used to.
mature

6. Arizona's **usual weather** is very dry.
climate

7. My parents **do not allow** television during the week.
forbid

8. Even though I'm dieting, I find it hard to **avoid giving in to my wish for** fried foods.
resist

9. If you apply heat to a compost pile, it speeds up the **process of the breaking down** of vegetable matter.
decay

10. It was such a(n) **extremely hot** day that the plants on our front steps were all drooping.
sorching

2C Applying Meanings

Circle the letter of each correct answer to the questions below. A question may have more than one correct answer.

1. Which of the following could be thought of as **towering**?
   (a) an eight-foot person
   (b) an eight-foot tree
   (c) a 100-foot flagpole
   (d) a 100-meter race

2. For which of the following might you need a **permit?**
   (a) camping in a park
   (b) setting lobster traps
   (c) keeping a dog
   (d) owning a goldfish

3. Which of the following help(s) the body to **resist** disease?
   (a) greasy food
   (b) exercise
   (c) germs
   (d) clothing

4. Which of the following **decay(s)?**
   (a) snow and ice
   (b) metal posts
   (c) fallen trees
   (d) cut grass

5. Which of the following are **forbidden?**
   (a) stealing
   (b) cheating
   (c) breathing
   (d) speeding

6. Which of the following can be **scorched?**
   (a) the bark of a tree
   (b) a new shirt
   (c) a clever idea
   (d) a pool of water

affect
calculate
climate
column
decay
exceed
forbid
grove
limb
mammoth
mature
permit
resist
scorch
tower

7. In which of the following might you see a **grove** of trees?

(a) a large park   (c) a parking lot

(b) a large field   (d) a tall building

8. Which of the following is a **limb**?

(a) a bird's wing   (c) a tree branch

(b) a bird's leg   (d) a tree root

2D Word Study

Antonyms are pairs of words whose meanings are opposite or nearly opposite each other. *Enter* and *exit* are antonyms. *Enter* means "to go in," and *exit* means "to go out."

Look at the words below. Circle the two words in each group of four that are antonyms.

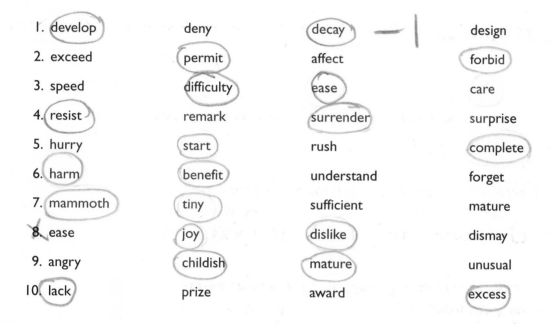

1. develop	deny	decay	design
2. exceed	permit	affect	forbid
3. speed	difficulty	ease	care
4. resist	remark	surrender	surprise
5. hurry	start	rush	complete
6. harm	benefit	understand	forget
7. mammoth	tiny	sufficient	mature
8. ease	joy	dislike	dismay
9. angry	childish	mature	unusual
10. lack	prize	award	excess

2E Passage

Read the passage below; then complete the exercise that follows.

California's Forest Giants

Along the coast of northern California grow huge, **towering** trees whose trunks look like the **columns** of a great Greek temple. These are redwood trees—the tallest of all trees—so tall, in fact, that they can reach 385 feet. Their trunks can grow straight up for 150 feet before the first **limbs** branch out. One redwood, called the Rockefeller Tree, is as tall as a thirty-five-story skyscraper!

Redwoods are so special that in some parts of California state laws **forbid** people to cut them down. In other parts of the state, where logging is **permitted**, redwood is sold for outside building and outdoor furniture because it does not **decay** as quickly as other kinds of wood.

Another giant California tree is the sequoia, a tree that is slightly shorter than a redwood. Sequoias prefer the colder, drier **climate** found farther inland on the slopes of the Sierra Nevada. They have thicker trunks and contain more wood than redwoods. In fact, it has been **calculated** that a full-grown sequoia contains enough wood to build thirty houses. The **mammoth** General Grant sequoia is almost a hundred feet around. It would take twenty people with arms stretched out to join hands around it! Cutting down any sequoia is not allowed.

Redwoods and sequoias are among the oldest living things: the age of some of them **exceeds** three thousand years. One of the reasons they live so long is that when they are **mature**, their bark is more than a foot thick. Forest fires that destroy other trees may **scorch** their outside bark, but do not **affect** them. The thick bark also helps them to **resist** diseases that kill other trees.

Yosemite National Park and Sequoia National Park, both in eastern California, are the best places to see sequoias. The best place to see redwoods is in Redwood National Park, in northwest California. In addition to its **groves** of redwoods, this park also contains forty miles of unspoiled Pacific coastline. These parks are among the most popular tourist attractions in the country.

Answer each of the following questions in the form of a sentence. If a question does not contain a vocabulary word from this lesson's word list, use one in your answer. Use each word only once. Questions and answers will then contain all fifteen words (or forms of the words).

1. What happens to sequoias and redwoods in a forest fire?

The forest fire did not affect sequoias and redwoods because their bark is thick.

2. Where can you find **groves** of redwoods?

The best place to see a redwood is in Redwood National Park.

3. If you lived in California, could you cut down a redwood tree?

Only in some parts of California where two logging is permited.

4. How far from the ground are the lowest branches of the redwoods?

Their limbs can grow 150 feet from the ground.

5. What do the trunks of redwoods look like?

The trunks look like the columns of a Greek Temple.

6. How old are the oldest sequoia and redwood trees?

Some of them exceeds three thousand years.

7. Why is **towering** a good word to use to describe these trees?

Towering is a good word to describe these trees because some trees can be 35 stories high.

8. When is their bark thickest?

Their bark is thick when there mature.

9. How else does their thick bark help the trees?

The bark helps resist diseases.

10. Could you cut down a sequoia?

You are not forbidden to cut down a sequoia tree.

11. Why is redwood used for building outside furniture?

The wood does not decay like other woods.

12. Why don't sequoias grow along the coast?

Sequoias prefer the colder, drier climate

13. How thick is the trunk of the General Grant tree?

The mammoth General Grant tree almost hundred feet from the ground.

14. How much wood does a full-grown sequoia contain?

It has been calculated that a full-grown sequoia can build 30 houses.

15. Why have redwoods and sequoias lived so long?

When there mature their bark is a foot thick.

FUN & FASCINATING FACTS

An easy way to learn simple arithmetic is to set out pebbles in a row. By adding more pebbles and counting the total, or by taking some away and counting the ones that remain, one can see the results of addition and subtraction. By using rows of pebbles, one can also learn multiplication. Pebbles arranged in three rows of four can be counted one at a time to see that 3 times 4 equals 12. By separating the pebbles into equal-sized groups, one can also learn division. For example, dividing the pebbles into two equal groups and counting the pebbles in one of them shows that 12 divided by 2 equals six. The Romans long ago thought of this method of doing math. In fact, our word **calculate** comes from the Latin word *calculus*, which means—a pebble!

Tens of thousands of years ago, a giant elephant lived in Europe and North America. It was called a mammoth. It was much bigger than today's elephants; the largest ones were almost fourteen feet from the ground to the shoulder. It had huge tusks that curved downward and a thick, hairy coat. Mammoths died out long ago, but the bodies of some of them were frozen solid in the cold northern regions of Canada and Russia. They are sometimes discovered when the ice around them melts. Because of this creature's great size, its name became the adjective **mammoth**, meaning "very large; huge."

Lesson 3

Word List Study the definitions of the words below; then do the exercises for the lesson.

approach
ə prōch´

v. To go closer to.
The vet **approached** the wounded deer carefully.
n. 1. A coming closer.
My grandparents dread the **approach** of winter.
2. A road or way that leads to a place.
The **approach** to the beach was blocked by a fallen tree.

burrow
bʉr´ ō

v. 1. To dig a hole or tunnel into or under something.
Turtles **burrow** into soft sand to lay their eggs.
2. To dig deeply into; to search.
The clerk **burrowed** through the pile of papers on his desk.
n. A hole or tunnel dug by an animal as a home or for protection.
A mole spends most of its time in its **burrow**.

cease
sēs

v. To stop; to come or bring to an end.
After several hours of thunder and lightning, the storm finally **ceased**.

destructive
di struk´ tiv

adj. Causing harm or damage.
Cutworms are very **destructive** garden insects.
destruction *n.* Harm or damage.
When Hurricane Katrina hit the Louisiana coast, it caused great **destruction**.

drowsy
drou´ zē

adj. Tired or sleepy.
Lying in the sun always makes my cat, Inky, **drowsy**.

famished
fa´ misht

adj. Very hungry.
Sometimes I work through my lunch hour, so by suppertime I am **famished**!

forecast
fôr´ kast

v. To figure out and say what will happen before it takes place.
Our fishing guide **forecast** a good catch.
n. A telling of what will happen.
As soon as Carlos gets up, he turns on the weather **forecast**.

hibernate
hī´ bər nāt

v. To spend the winter in a resting state.
Bears **hibernate** because they can't find enough food in the winter.

migrate
mī´ grāt

v. To move from one country or region to another.
Hundreds of thousands of people have **migrated** to the United States in search of freedom.
migration *n.* The act of migrating.
My friend Sandhya is studying Indian **migration** to the United States.
migratory (mī´ grə tôr ē) *adj.* Moving from one place or country to another, usually regularly.
Canada geese are **migratory** birds.

nestle
ne´ səl

v. 1. To settle down comfortably, as if in a nest.
"The children were **nestled** all snug in their beds" is a famous line from '*Twas the Night before Christmas.*
2. To lie in a sheltered, partly hidden place.
The little Swiss town **nestled** at the foot of the Alps.

observe
əb zurv´

v. 1. To see; to notice.
I looked up at the sky and **observed** a hawk circling slowly, far above us.
2. To comment; to remark.
Sleepily, I **observed** that it was time we left.
3. To mark an event or day.
We **observed** Martin Luther King Day by closing the store.
4. To obey.
I try to **observe** the speed limit when I drive.

prepare
pri par´

v. To make or get ready.
The scouts **prepared** for their camping trip by getting lots of freeze-dried food.
preparation (pre pə rā´ shən) *n.* Something done to get ready.
Antonio and Ruth did most of the **preparation** for the cookout the night before.

reduce
ri do͞os´

v. To make or become smaller or less.
This winter, Vermont **reduced** the amount of salt it put on its roads.
reduction (ri duk´ shən) *n.* The act of reducing or the amount by which something is reduced.
The store sold out of swimsuits after its huge price **reduction**.

severe
sə vir´

adj. 1. Very strict or harsh.
That's a very **severe** punishment for turning a paper in late.
2. Hard to bear or deal with.
A **severe** frost caused a lot of damage to central Florida's orange crop.

venture
ven´ chər

v. To dare to do, to go, or to say.
Maria **ventured** onto the dance floor even though she didn't know how to dance.
n. Something that involves the risk of a loss.
Grandpa's most successful **venture** was a carpet cleaning service.

3A Finding Meanings

Choose two phrases to form a sentence that correctly uses a word from Word List 3. Write each sentence in the space provided.

100

1. (a) does a lot of damage.
   (b) A migratory animal is one that
   (c) can be easily tamed.
   (d) A destructive animal is one that

A destructive animal is one that does a lot of damage.

2. (a) a disappearance.
   (b) A venture is
   (c) An approach is
   (d) a coming closer.

An approach is a coming closer.

3. (a) A famished creature   (c) moves with the changing seasons.
   (b) A migratory creature   (d) goes to sleep for the winter.

A migorty creature moves with the changing seasons.

4. (a) To burrow is to   (c) refuse to obey.
   (b) dig a hole or tunnel.   (d) To nestle is to

To burrow is to dig a hole or tunnel.

5. (a) to take no part in it.   (c) to say it will happen.
   (b) To forecast an event is   (d) To observe an event is

To forecast an event is to say it will happen.

6. (a) To reduce is to   (c) To nestle is to
   (b) settle down comfortably. (d) fall into a deep sleep.

To nestle is to settle down comfortably.

7. (a) Preparation is   (c) Hibernation is
   (b) what you do to get ready. (d) what is asked for.

Preparation is what you do to get ready.

8. (a) something that involves a risk.   (c) A reduction is
   (b) the addition of something.   (d) A venture is

A venture is something that involves a risk.

9. (a) very thirsty.   (c) To be famished is to be
   (b) very hungry.   (d) To be drowsy is to be

To be famished is to be very hungry.

10. (a) To observe something is to   (c) To cease something is to
    (b) pay no attention to it.   (d) notice it.

To observe something is to notice it.

3B Just the Right Word

Improve each of the following sentences by crossing out the bold phrase and replacing it with a word (or a form of the word) from Word List 3.

90

1. Hana was starting to feel ~~very sleepy~~ *drowsy* when a loud noise made her jump.

2. The rain did not ~~come to an end~~ *cease* until early the next morning.

3. Some animals ~~go into a long, deep sleep~~ *hibernate* because there is so little for them to eat during the winter months.

4. The cottage *nestled* lay partly hidden in a hollow beside a grove of poplar trees.

5. All the *approaches* roads that lead to the airport are closed because of the snowstorm.

6. The *migration* long journey of Canada geese from northern Canada to South America occurs each fall.

7. Even though Granny has *severe* very bad arthritis, she still tries to walk every day.

8. The *reduction* cutting down in size of this week's newspaper to just four pages was due to the paper shortage.

9. Ron *burrowed* dug deeply through the papers on his desk, trying to find the letter from his father.

10. As Maria Tipo played the piano, I *observed* closely watched the way she used the pedal.

3C Applying Meanings

Circle the letter of each correct answer to the questions below. A question may have more than one correct answer.

1. Which of the following can people **reduce**?
   (a) their weight √
   (b) their shoe size
   (c) their age
   (d) their spending √

2. Which of the following would be a **severe** punishment?
   (a) a slap on the wrist ✓
   (b) going to jail ✓
   (c) no television for a day
   (d) being told to be quiet

3. Which of the following can a person **forecast**?
   (a) the result of a game √
   (b) the weather √
   (c) a past event
   (d) costs of doing business ✓

4. Which of the following can cause **destruction**?
   (a) forest fires √
   (b) floods √
   (c) bombs
   (d) hurricanes ✓

5. Which of the following could **cease**?
   (a) fighting √
   (b) noises √
   (c) the weather
   (d) a storm ✗

approach
burrow
cease
destructive
drowsy
famished
forecast
hibernate
migrate
nestle
observe
prepare
reduce
severe
venture

6. Which of the following can **migrate**?
   (a) animals ✓   (c) plants
   (b) birds ✓   (d) humans ✓

7. Which of the following could be **observed**?
   (a) a law ✓   (c) a rule ✓
   (b) a birthday   (d) a full moon ✓

8. Which of the following can be **prepared**?
   (a) a lunch for four ✓   (c) a book report ✓
   (b) a garden for planting ✓   (d) a full moon

3D Word Study

Many of our English words come to us from Latin. We say they have Latin roots. Our word *patriot*, for example, is formed from the Latin word *pater*, meaning "father."

— 3

To the right of each vocabulary word, write the Latin word that it comes from, together with its meaning. Choose from the ten Latin roots listed below.

propius (near)   *plere* (complete)   *bene* (well)   *calculus* (pebble)   *severus* (serious; strict)

hibernus (winter)   *fames* (hunger)   *servare* (watch)   *jacere* (throw)   *cessare* (stop)

Definition	English Word	Latin Word	Meaning
1. to draw near; to get closer	approach	prpius	to draw near
2. to spend the winter sleeping	hibernate	hibernus	to spend the winter sleeping
3. very hungry; starving	famished	fames	starving
4. to bring to an end; to finish	complete	plere	to finish and
5. to come to an end; to stop	cease	cessare	to stop
6. to look at closely	observe	observe	to look closely
7. strict or harsh	severe	severe	strict or harsh
8. to throw onto a screen	project	project	to throw onto a screen
9. to be useful to; to help	benefit	benefit	to help
10. to figure out using math	calculate	calcuate	to figure out using math.

3E Passage

Read the passage below; then complete the exercise that follows.

A Long Winter Nap

Summer is a good time of year for most animals. It's easy for them to keep warm, and food is plentiful. Winter is harder for them. Lakes and ponds are frozen, snow may cover the ground, and food is much harder to find. Many birds and some animals escape northern winters by **migrating** south in the fall and returning in the spring.

The woodchuck, or groundhog, as it is also called, deals with winter differently. It **hibernate**s. As soon as it feels the weather turning cold, it digs a **burrow** at least five feet underground and makes a comfortable nest with leaves and grass. It spends the cold winter months **nestled** in its underground bed, and does not usually wake up until spring. It is far enough below ground so that there is no danger that it will freeze to death even during the most **severe** winter.

Since it will not eat at all during the winter, the woodchuck eats as much and as often as it can during the summer. People with gardens know how **destructive** one can be to their plants. As winter **approaches**, the woodchuck becomes so fat it can hardly move. It gets ready for its long sleep by **preparing** its nest and closing off the openings of the tunnels that lead down to it. When it starts to feel **drowsy,** it makes itself comfortable and falls into a long, deep sleep that can last up to eight months.

If you **observed** the woodchuck in this state, you might think it had died. Its breathing almost **ceases**, and its heart slows down to about four beats a minute. If you took its temperature, you would find that it had fallen to just above freezing. When the woodchuck wakes up in the spring after going without food for so many months, its weight has been **reduced** to only half of what it was in the fall. Almost all its body fat has been used up to keep it alive during its long sleep. By February or March, the **famished** animal is ready to leave its hole and go looking for its first meal.

Years ago, people who lived in the country eagerly awaited the sight of the first groundhog putting its head above ground; it was a sign that winter was over. This gave rise to a number of stories. One of them, told by German farmers who had settled in Punxsutawney, Pennsylvania, was about a groundhog they called Punxsutawney Phil. This remarkable animal could **forecast** the weather.

According to the story, Phil **ventured** from his nest every February 2. He poked his head above ground and looked around. If he saw his shadow, it meant that there would be another month and a half of winter, so he went back to sleep for another six weeks. If the weather was cloudy, and he didn't see his shadow, it meant spring would be early. This story spread around the country, and February 2 became known as Groundhog Day.

approach
burrow
cease
destructive
drowsy
famished
forecast
hibernate
migrate
nestle
observe
prepare
reduce
severe
venture

Answer each of the following questions in the form of a sentence. If a question does not contain a vocabulary word from this lesson's word list, use one in your answer. Use each word only once. Questions and answers will then contain all fifteen words (or forms of the words).

1. Why do you almost never see woodchucks in winter? *hibernate* *hibernate*

Woodchucks hibernate every winter.

2. What **preparations** does a woodchuck make for winter? *drowsy* *prep*

When woodchucks feel drowsy they prepare for the deep long sleep.

3. How does the woodchuck's appearance change as winter **approaches**? *nestles* *approach*

It nestles to there nest. ✗

4. How does a woodchuck feel just before it begins its long sleep? *drowsy*

A woodchuck feels really drowsy

5. How do woodchucks keep from freezing during the winter months? *ceases* *reduce* ?

It keeps temprature above freazing

6. What might the temperature be during a **severe** winter?

Very cold.

7. How do we know that a woodchuck needs only a little oxygen during its winter sleep? *ceases*

It makes a closing off the opening of the tunnels that lead to it.

8. What does the woodchuck do when it gets into its **burrow**?

They fall into a deep sleep.

9. How does the woodchuck's size change over the winter? *reduced*

Woodchucks reduced there weight.

10. What is the meaning of **observe** as it is used in the passage?

To inspect their breathing.

11. Why is the woodchuck **famished** when it wakes up in early spring?

They hadn't ate for a long time.

12. What was unusual about Punxsutawney Phil? [forecast]

He tells the forecast.

13. What is supposed to happen on Groundhog Day? [ventures]

Phil ventures out of his nest and looks around

14. What do many northern birds do to escape the winter? [migrate]

They migrate to the south.

15. Why do gardeners think woodchucks are **destructive**?

Woodchucks might eat there crops

FUN & FASCINATING FACTS

French, Spanish, and Italian are Latin languages. This means that many of their words come directly from the Latin that people throughout the Roman Empire spoke two thousand years ago. For example, you learned the Latin word *hibernum*, meaning *winter*. The French word for *winter*, *hiver*, also comes from Latin.

When modern science began several hundred years ago, there was a need for scientific terms, and these were usually formed from Latin, the language of scholars. The word **hibernate** was formed in this way. It means "to go into a sleeplike state during the winter," and comes from the Latin word for *winter*.

Lesson 4

> ## Word List
Study the definitions of the words below; then do the exercises for the lesson.

active
ak´ tiv

adj. 1. Taking part; working.
Luis has been an **active** member of the chess club for two years.
2. Lively; quick; busy.
Even though she is over ninety, Dr. O'Brien still has a very **active** mind.
3. Moving a lot; moving quickly.
Since I've been more physically **active**, I can run around the track more easily.

astound
ə stound´

v. To surprise; to amaze.
The United States **astounded** the world in 1969 by landing people on the moon.
astounding   *adj.* Very surprising.
The report of flying saucers landing on the White House lawn would be **astounding** if it were true.

attend
ə tend´

v. 1. To go to or be present at.
If you are planning to **attend** the lunchroom committee meeting, please let Mr. Minh know.
2. To pay attention to.
The judge asked the jury to **attend** carefully to what she was going to say.

cherish
cher´ ish

v. 1. To cling to an idea or feeling.
Ramona **cherished** the hope that her father would return soon.
2. To take good care of; to love.
I **cherish** the gold watch my grandfather gave me.

contract
kən trakt´

v. 1. To make an agreement that has the force of law.
We **contracted** with carpenters to repair the stairs.
2. To get; to come to have.
When I **contracted** chicken pox, Dr. Robey told me I had to stay away from other people.
3. To make or become smaller.
By 1828, Cherokee lands had **contracted** to one-tenth the size they had been a hundred years earlier.
n. (kän´ trakt) An agreement that has the force of law.
Tom has just signed a **contract** with a publisher for his first book on the copper miners.

eager
ē´ gər

adj. Wanting very much.
We were **eager** to take part in the science project.
eagerly   *adv.* With a great deal of enthusiasm, wanting.
We **eagerly** awaited the arrival of our cousins, whom we hadn't seen in several months.

expose
ek spōz´

v. 1. To make known.
In her weekly newspaper column, Molly Ivins **expose**d the plan to cut health benefits.
2. To open to view.
Cleaning the painting **exposed** the original colors.
3. To leave unprotected.
Since I had no place to keep my bike, I had to leave it outside, **exposed** to the weather.

grace
grās

n. 1. Beauty of form or movement.
Margot Fonteyn danced with such **grace** that she was hailed as one of the world's greatest ballerinas.
2. A short prayer said before a meal.
They always say **grace** in her family.
3. An extra period to do or pay something.
The painters had three days **grace** to finish the house.
graceful   *adj.* Having beauty of movement.
With a **graceful** leap, the cat landed on my lap.

impose
im pōz´

v. 1. To force someone to accept or put up with.
The new coach **imposed** strict rules about arriving late or leaving practice early.
2. To take unfair advantage of.
I try not to **impose** on my mother's good nature.

modest
mä´ dəst

adj. 1. Not thinking too highly of oneself.
Nadia was too **modest** to accept all the credit for her part in producing the play.
2. Simple; not fancy or extreme.
The Wallmans lived in the same **modest** apartment all their lives.
modesty   *n.* The quality of being modest.
My sense of **modesty** keeps me from taking too much credit for the project's success.

parallel
par´ ə lel

adj. Lying in the same direction and always the same distance apart.
The two edges of a ruler are **parallel**.

paralyze
par´ ə līz

v. 1. To stop all movement or feeling in.
As the huge wave approached, fear **paralyzed** people walking at the water's edge and they stood there motionless.
2. To make helpless or powerless.
The snowstorm **paralyzed** Washington D.C. for five days.
paralysis (pə ra´ lə səs) *n.* Condition of being paralyzed.
President Franklin D. Roosevelt used a wheelchair because of the **paralysis** of his legs.

pessimist
pe´ sə mist

n. A person who expects things to turn out badly.
A **pessimist** carries an umbrella even though the forecast is for fine weather.
pessimistic   *adj.* Not having hope, joy, or confidence; gloomy.
After losing her librarian's job, Ms. Merkelson was **pessimistic** about finding another library position in the same town.

recite
ri sīt´

v. To say aloud before an audience, usually from memory.
Rozzie **recited** her favorite Emily Dickinson poem to the class.
recital   *n.* A program of music or dance.
I felt very nervous before my ballet **recital**.

respond
ri spänd´

v. To answer.
When you want to **respond** to a question, please raise your hand.
response   *n.* Something said or done in reply.
Henry took a few moments to think before giving his **response** to Mr. Bartlett's question.

4A Finding Meanings

Choose two phrases to form a sentence that correctly uses a word from Word List 4. Write each sentence in the space provided.

1. (a) to love that person.   (c) To expose someone is
   (b) To cherish someone is   (d) to fear that person.

To cherish someone is to love that person.

2. (a) A response is   (c) Paralysis is
   (b) an increase in size.   (d) an answer.

A response is an answer.

3. (a) that causes shock and surprise.   (c) An eager reply is one
   (b) An astounding reply is one   (d) that is not spoken.

An astounding reply is one that causes shock and surprise.

4. (a) To contract is   (c) to make an agreement.
   (b) To attend is   (d) to be afraid.

To contract is to make an agreement.

5. (a) are not hidden from view.   (c) Parallel beams
   (b) Exposed beams   (d) meet at a corner.

Exposed beams are not hidden from view.

6. (a) To attend a speech is   (c) to make changes in it.
   (b) To recite a speech is   (d) to be present at it.

To recite a speech is to be present at it.

7. (a) affects an interest in something.   (c) A pessimistic person
   (b) An eager person   (d) is quick to take part in something.

An eager person is quick to take part in something.

8. (a) Graceful lines are   (c) the same distance apart.
   (b) Parallel lines are   (d) curving away from each other.

Parallel lines are curving away from each other

9. (a) a loss of the ability to move.   (c) a belief that things will turn out badly.
   (b) Modesty is   (d) Paralysis is

Paralysis is a loss of the abillity to move.

8/9

10. (a) A recital is
    (b) a written agreement.
    (c) A pessimist is
    (d) one who is gloomy.

A pessimist is one that is gloomy.

11. (a) Grace is
    (b) Modesty is
    (c) beauty of movement.
    (d) failing to do what is right.

Grace is beauty of movement.

4B Just the Right Word

Improve each of the following sentences by crossing out the bold phrase and replacing it with a word (or a form of the word) from Word List 4.

1. Where the paint has peeled off the house, the wood will be **left unprotected** [exposed] and unable to stand up to scorching summer heat and severe winter cold.

2. The magician promised that his next trick would **create great amazement in** us. [astound]

3. Eleanor Roosevelt's **lack of feelings of self-importance** impressed all who knew her. [modesty]

4. Heavy snow **stopped the movement of** traffic in Denver for two days. [paralyzed]

5. The librarian gave me one week's **extra time** to pay the fine. [grace]

6. Only about half of the members of the gardening club are **taking part in what is going on**. [astounding / active]

7. Unfortunately, my roomate is a **person who usually expects things to turn out badly**, so he's not a very cheerful person to live with. [pessimist]

8. I was afraid I was **forcing myself on them** when I stayed an extra week at the Mendelssohns. [imposing]

9. The pupil of the eye **becomes smaller** in bright light. [contracted]

10. Did you **give your attention to** the dinner invitation from Aunt Helen? [respond]

active
astound
attend
cherish
contract
eager
expose
grace
impose
modest
parallel
paralyze
pessimist
recite
respond

4C Applying Meanings

Circle the letter of each correct answer to the questions below. A question may have more than one correct answer.

1. Which of the following could a person **attend**?
    (a) a benefit
    (b) a concert
    (c) a meeting
    (d) a remark

2. Which of the following can be **contracted**?
   - (a) an illness
   - (c) muscles
   - (b) the pupils of the eyes
   - (d) a habit

3. Which of the following requires a person to be **active**?
   - (a) playing hockey
   - (c) walking the dog
   - (b) washing windows
   - (d) watching television

4. Which of the following can be **paralyzed**?
   - (a) a person's lower limbs
   - (c) a person's hair
   - (b) a person's body
   - (d) a person's clothes

5. Which of the following might a **modest** person say?
   - (a) "I had very little to do with it."
   - (c) "You deserve all the credit."
   - (b) "Please don't bother to thank me."
   - (d) "I am the greatest!"

6. Which of the following might a **pessimistic** person say?
   - (a) "Everything will be all right."
   - (c) "We're bound to lose."
   - (b) "It's no use trying."
   - (d) "Next time we'll try harder."

7. Which of the following are **parallel**?
   - (a) the opposite sides of a square
   - (c) the letters A, E, and O
   - (b) the three sides of a triangle
   - (d) the numbers 1, 2, and 3

8. Which of the following would you expect to be **graceful**?
   - (a) a beginning skier
   - (c) a Broadway dancer
   - (b) an Olympic diver
   - (d) an Olympic skater

4D Word Study

Look at the words below. Circle the two words that are synonyms in each group of four.

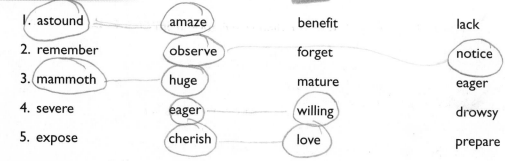

1. astound	amaze	benefit	lack
2. remember	observe	forget	notice
3. mammoth	huge	mature	eager
4. severe	eager	willing	drowsy
5. expose	cherish	love	prepare

Circle the two words that are antonyms in each group of four below.

6. pessimistic   remarkable   sufficient   hopeful

7. drowsy   modest   complete   active

8. boastful   destructive   famished   modest

9. recite   expose   impose   hide

10. approach   migrate   enlarge   reduce

4E Passage

Read the passage below; then complete the exercise that follows.

One Step at a Time

Sucheng Chan was an **active** child who loved to run outside and play with the other children in the village in China where she was born. But in 1943, when she was four years old, she **contracted** polio, a childhood disease that can make people very sick and often causes **paralysis**. The muscles in her legs slowly wasted away, and she could no longer run or even walk. The doctors were **pessimistic** about her chances of living more than a year or two. They did not know what a determined person Sucheng Chan was.

After lying helplessly in bed for three years, Sucheng Chan surprised her mother one day by asking her to set up some chairs in two **parallel** lines, their backs facing. She then forced herself out of bed and made her way between the chairs, using their backs as support. She did this time after time, her body aching from many falls.

China was at war with Japan during these years, and Sucheng Chan's father was serving in the army, unable to see his family. He **cherished** his daughter, and it saddened him that he could not give her the comfort and support she needed. When the war ended and he returned home, he was **astounded** to see Sucheng Chan walk up to him and welcome him. Her movements were jerky and not at all **graceful**, but to her father there had never been such a beautiful sight.

Sucheng Chan had always been a bright child who was **eager** to go to school. But in those days in China education was not free, and her parents had only a **modest** income. Sucheng Chan was eight years old before they had saved enough money for her to **attend** the American school in Shanghai. There she learned to speak English and began a lifelong study of Asian history.

In 1948, at the end of Sucheng Chan's first year in school, China's government became communist. The new government **imposed** strict rules forbidding contact with foreigners. One result of these measures was that the American school was closed. Sucheng Chan and her parents grew increasingly unhappy. They decided to leave China and settle in Malaysia.

Sucheng Chan's teenage years, which she spent in a Malaysian high school, were the happiest of her life. She did very well in school and took piano lessons, sometimes giving **recitals** for visitors. Once, while walking across the stage, her legs gave way and she fell. She heard a voice say, "Ayah! A baikah (cripple) should not **expose** herself like that." Sucheng Chan's **response** was to struggle to her feet, walk to the piano, sit down, and play so beautifully that the audience was moved to tears.

After graduating from high school, Sucheng Chan went on to win scholarships to the University of Hawaii. She later became a professor of history and director of Asian American studies at the University of California, Santa Barbara, leading a full and active life. Doctors told her that she might need a wheelchair by the time she was forty because polio can come back, causing more damage to muscles. They were right. But, she said, "I use it only when I am *not* in a hurry."

active

astound

attend

cherish

contract

eager

expose

grace

impose

modest

parallel

paralyze

pessimist

recite

respond

Answer each of the following questions in the form of a sentence. If a question does not contain a vocabulary word from this lesson's word list, use one in your answer. Use each word only once. Questions and answers will then contain all fifteen words (or forms of the words).

1. Why didn't Sucheng Chan go to school until she was eight?

In those days in China education was not free her parents had only a modest income.

2. Why did it become impossible for Sucheng Chan to run outside and play?

Sucheng Chan got paralyzed due to polio.

3. Did her doctors expect Sucheng Chan to get better?

The doctors were pessimistic about her chances of living more than a year.

4. What usually happens to people who **contract** polio?

That can make people very sick.

5. What is the meaning of **active** as it is used in the passage?

A person who is active likes to run and play.

6. How does the passage suggest that her father often thought of Sucheng Chan while he was away?

He cherished his daughter it saddened him that he can't give her comfort.

7. Why was Sucheng Chan's father **astounded** when he saw his daughter after the war?

Sucheng Chan walked up to him.

8. Why wasn't Sucheng Chan **graceful**?

She wasn't graceful because she walked jerky.

9. How did Sucheng Chan feel about going to school?

She felt really eager to go to school.

10. What is the meaning of **attend** as it is used in the passage?

To attend a American school.

11. Why don't **parallel** lines ever meet?

They are always the same distance apart.

12. Why do you think China **imposed** rules against contact with foreigners?

China thinks foreigners are bad.

13. How can you tell that Sucheng Chan played the piano well?

She gave recitals to visitors.

14. What did the person who remarked that Sucheng Chan "should not **expose** herself like that" expect her to do?

For her not to preform in public.

15. What might Sucheng Chan's **response** have been if she were not such a determined person?

She might cry and refuse to preform.

FUN & FASCINATING FACTS

Antonyms are words that are opposite in meaning. The antonym of *contract* in its meaning of "to make or become smaller" is *expand*. Metals contract as they get colder; they expand as they get warmer.

Pessimist and *optimist* are another pair of antonyms. An *optimist* has a cheerful outlook on life and expects things to go well. *Pessimist* is formed from the Latin word *pessimus*, which means "worst." *Optimist* is formed from the Latin word *optimus*, which means "best." There is a saying that a pessimist is a person who looks upon the glass as being half-empty; an optimist is a person who looks upon it as being half-full.

Review for Lessons 1-4

Crossword Puzzle Solve the crossword puzzle below by studying the clues and filling in the answer boxes. Clues followed by a number are definitions of vocabulary words in Lessons 1 through 4. The number gives the lesson from which the answer to the clue is taken.

Clues Across

1. Having no missing parts (1)
5. To rot (2)
8. To be present at (4)
10. To speak (1)
12. The Atlantic _____
13. To make less painful (1)
14. One, _____ , three
16. To make larger or better (1)
18. To make ready (3)
20. A group of trees growing together (2)
23. A stomach _____
26. To burn slightly (2)
29. Lively; quick; busy (4)
30. To cause feelings of fear, worry, or surprise (1)
31. To greet or welcome (1)
32. A hole or tunnel dug by an animal (3)
33. Very high (2)
34. Very strict or harsh (3)

Clues Down

2. Fully grown (2)
3. Wanting very much to do or get (4)
4. To dare to do, to go, or to say (3)
6. To go beyond something (2)
7. The _____ is a famous fort in San Antonio.
9. To draw in an aimless kind of way
11. Something said or expressed (1)
15. To come closer (3)
17. Loss of ability to do or feel (4)
19. Something laid by a bird
21. A paper allowing a person to do something (2)
22. One who loves and supports his country (1)
24. The average weather conditions of an area (2)
25. To lie in a sheltered, partly hidden place (3)
27. A row of figures running down a page (2)
28. Red and blue, for example

Lesson 5

Word List
Study the definitions of the words below; then do the exercises for the lesson.

abrupt
ə brupt´

adj. Happening suddenly, without warning.
When the bus made an **abrupt** stop, several people were thrown off balance.

achieve
ə chēv´

v. To do what one sets out to do.
Even though she was blind and deaf, Helen Keller **achieved** her goal of graduating from college.
achievement *n.* Something done that takes skill or effort.
Landing astronauts on the moon was a great **achievement**.

attempt
ə tempt´

v. To try; to make an effort.
When I **attempted** to leave class early, the teacher asked me to wait until the period was over.
n. A try.
The athlete cleared the bar in the high jump on her third **attempt**.

contempt
kən tempt´

n. A feeling that someone or something is bad or unworthy.
Their classmates felt nothing but **contempt** for those who refused to help the new student.

entertain
en tər tān´

v. 1. To interest and amuse.
My little brother Ramon **entertained** himself for hours with his new paints.
2. To have guests.
We **entertained** some old friends on Thanksgiving weekend.
3. To have in mind.
Lin is **entertaining** the idea of going to soccer camp next summer.

glimpse
glimps

v. To get a quick look at.
I **glimpsed** a black bear near our campground.
n. A quick or hasty look.
I was thrilled to get a **glimpse** of Pavarotti leaving the opera house.

mock
mäk

v. To make fun of.
Cinderella's stepsisters **mocked** her for thinking she could go to the ball.
adj. Not real; pretended.
Mock turtle soup is really made of veal broth, not turtle meat.

persist
pər sist´

v. 1. To keep on doing or trying.
In spite of many falls on the ice, I **persisted** and finally did a figure-eight.
2. To go on and on.
If this rain **persists**, we'll have to cut our vacation short.
persistence *n.* Sticking to something; not giving up.
Emil's **persistence** was rewarded when the tenth law school he applied to accepted him.
persistent *adj.* Refusing to give up.
The **persistent** reporter kept asking questions until she had found out all there was to know about the case.

persuade pər swād´	*v.* To win someone over by arguing or asking. Frank finally **persuaded** me to read *The Adventures of Tom Sawyer*. **persuasive** *adj.* Having the power to persuade. Mary was so **persuasive** that we agreed to help her paint her room.
phase fāz	*n.* A stage in a series of changes. The full moon is one of the **phases** of the moon.
quaint kwānt	*adj.* Odd or unusual in a pleasing or old-fashioned way. Wooden shoes seem **quaint** to Americans, but not to the people of Holland.
recall ri kôl´	*v.* 1. To remember. Do you **recall** what time we left for the soccer game? 2. To call or take back. The manufacturer **recalled** the cars because of a problem in the steering.
reject ri jekt´	*v.* To refuse to accept or use. The school board **rejected** the plan for the new gym because its cost was excessive. *n.* (rē´ jekt) Something that falls short of what is acceptable. Peter buys factory **rejects** at the pottery store for much less than the price of perfect pieces.
revise ri vīz´	*v.* 1. To go over carefully in order to correct or improve. I don't like to **revise** my stories, but I have to admit they get better when I do. 2. To change in order to bring up to date. The publishers of that dictionary **revise** it every eight or ten years.
sensitive sen´ sə tiv	*adj.* 1. Quick to notice or feel. My doctor is very **sensitive** to my feelings. 2. Easily affected by even slight change. Film used in cameras is very **sensitive** to light.

5A Finding Meanings

Choose two phrases to form a sentence that correctly uses a word from Word List 5. Write each sentence in the space provided.

1. (a) one stage in a process.
   (b) something overheard.
   (c) A glimpse is
   (d) A phase is

A phase is one stage in process.

2. (a) An achievement is
   (b) something done by making an effort.
   (c) Contempt is
   (d) something that is changed.

An achievement is something done by effort.

3. (a) loud noise.
   (b) quick look.
   (c) A glimpse is a
   (d) A reject is a

A glimpse is a quick look.

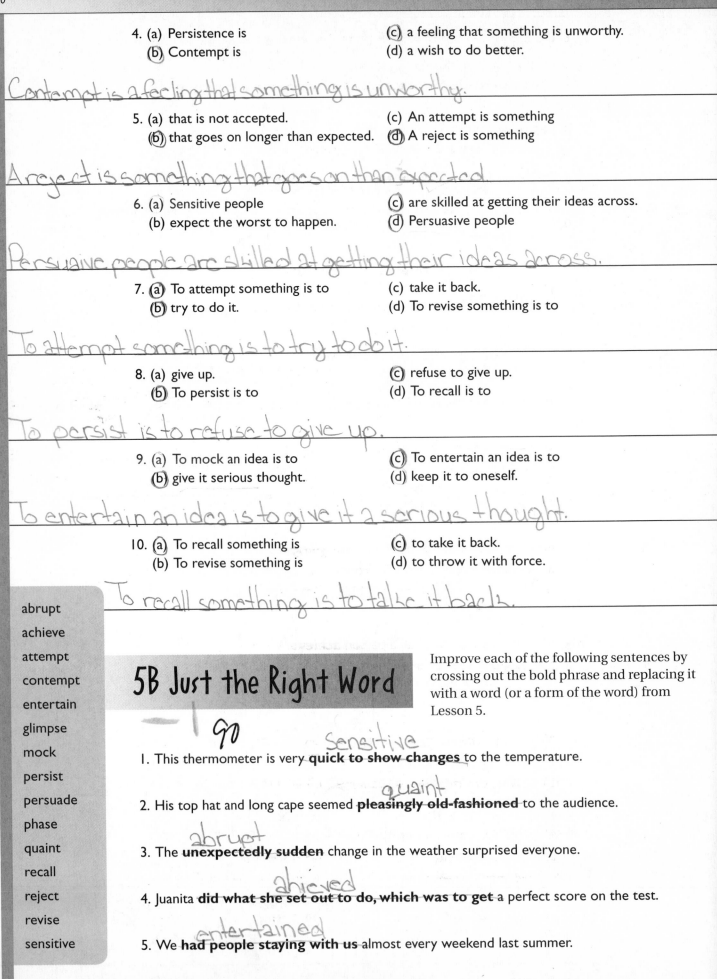

4. (a) Persistence is
   (b) Contempt is
   (c) a feeling that something is unworthy.
   (d) a wish to do better.

Contempt is a feeling that something is unworthy.

5. (a) that is not accepted.
   (b) that goes on longer than expected.
   (c) An attempt is something
   (d) A reject is something

A reject is something that goes on than expected.

6. (a) Sensitive people
   (b) expect the worst to happen.
   (c) are skilled at getting their ideas across.
   (d) Persuasive people

Persuasive people are skilled at getting their ideas across.

7. (a) To attempt something is to
   (b) try to do it.
   (c) take it back.
   (d) To revise something is to

To attempt something is to try to do it.

8. (a) give up.
   (b) To persist is to
   (c) refuse to give up.
   (d) To recall is to

To persist is to refuse to give up.

9. (a) To mock an idea is to
   (b) give it serious thought.
   (c) To entertain an idea is to
   (d) keep it to oneself.

To entertain an idea is to give it a serious thought.

10. (a) To recall something is
    (b) To revise something is
    (c) to take it back.
    (d) to throw it with force.

To recall something is to take it back.

abrupt
achieve
attempt
contempt
entertain
glimpse
mock
persist
persuade
phase
quaint
recall
reject
revise
sensitive

5B Just the Right Word

Improve each of the following sentences by crossing out the bold phrase and replacing it with a word (or a form of the word) from Lesson 5.

90

Sensitive
1. This thermometer is very **quick to show changes** to the temperature.

quaint
2. His top hat and long cape seemed **pleasingly old-fashioned** to the audience.

abrupt
3. The **unexpectedly sudden** change in the weather surprised everyone.

achieved
4. Juanita **did what she set out to do, which was to get** a perfect score on the test.

entertained
5. We **had people staying with us** almost every weekend last summer.

6. If the fog **goes on for a long time,** the plane will be unable to leave on time.
rejects

7. The coach **made fun of** the shortstop's unusual way of running.
mocked

8. I **caught a quick look at** him through the window of the bus.
glimpsed

9. She needs to **make changes in** her speech before she gives it.
revise

10. Each **stage in the series of changes** must be carefully planned or the project will fail.
phase

5C Applying Meanings

Circle the letter of each correct answer to the questions below. A question may have more than one correct answer.

1. Which of the following can be **sensitive?**
   (a) a person's clothing
   (b) a person's hearing
   (c) a person's fe____s
   (d) a person's ski___

2. Which of the following might a person think **quaint?**
   (a) a full moon
   (b) an old Valentine card
   (c) a hundred-year-old toy
   (d) pictures in a 1910 book of fairy tales

3. Which of the following might a person **glimpse?**
   (a) someone leaving a crowded room
   (b) a letter someone is trying to hide
   (c) a loud noise
   (d) a strange smell

4. Which of the following can a person **achieve?**
   (a) a goal one sets for oneself
   (b) a calm frame of mind
   (c) curly hair
   (d) high marks on a test

5. Which of the following would you probably **reject?**
   (a) a chance to attend college
   (b) an offer of a ride from a stranger
   (c) bad advice
   (d) an unworkable plan

6. Which of the following might be **persistent?**
   (a) a flash of lightning
   (b) cold and rainy weather
   (c) a back pain
   (d) a bad smell

7. Which of the following can be **revised**?
   (a) a written contract
   (b) a person's height
   (c) a set of calculations
   (d) a weather forecast

8. Which of the following might be **entertaining**?
   (a) a magician's tricks
   (b) a football game
   (c) a bus timetable
   (d) an aching tooth

5D Word Study

Some things have just one part, and some things have more than one part. A brick has just one part. So does a baseball bat. A box has a bottom, four sides, and a top. Your body is made up of a head, a trunk, and four limbs.

Some words, too, have just one part, and some words have more than one part. There are names for these different parts. The main part of a word is called its *root*. You will remember roots from Lesson 3. Our word *patriotic* is formed from the Latin root *pater*, meaning "father."

A *prefix* is the part of a word that comes before the root. The prefix *un-* turns a word into its opposite. It turns *interesting* into *uninteresting*. *In-* is another prefix that does the same thing. It turns *sane* into *insane*. Note that *in-* changes to *im-* before the *m* sound. This makes it easier to say.

Change each of the words below into its opposite by adding one of the following prefixes: *un-*, *in-*, or *im-*. Check each of your answers in a dictionary to be sure you have formed an actual word.

— 6

1. patriotic — unpatriotic
2. remarkable — unremarkable
3. mature — *Inmature*
4. affected — unaffected
5. sufficient — unsufficient / insufficent
6. complete — incomplete
7. developed — undeveloped
8. persuasive — impersuasive / unpersuasive
9. modest — unmodest / in modest
10. sensitive — unsensitive / im sensitive
11. active — unactive / inactive
12. prepared — inprepared / unprepared

abrupt
achieve
attempt
contempt
entertain
glimpse
mock
persist
persuade
phase
quaint
recall
reject
revise
sensitive

5E Passage

Read the passage below; then complete the exercise that follows.

A Life That Changed

Hans Christian Andersen's famous story "The Ugly Duckling" tells of a little duckling that looks different from others and is **mocked** by them for being odd. The little creature turns out not to be a duck at all but a beautiful swan. From a quick **glimpse** into the life of the author, we learn that a dramatic change took place in Andersen's own childhood, and that he also took a long time to fit in and to find a special place for himself.

Hans Christian Andersen was born in Denmark in 1805. His father was a shoemaker who struggled to make a living. Hans always felt loved by his parents, and had a happy childhood. He had no brothers or sisters, and he was a **sensitive** child who lived in a private world of his own. His greatest joy was a toy theater his father made for him. The little boy **entertained** his parents by putting on plays, dressing the people of his little toy theater in **quaint** clothes that he made himself.

When Hans was eleven his father died, and the young boy's life changed **abruptly**. He had to go to work, but he failed at every job he **attempted**. His fellow workers could not understand the strange boy who spent all his time daydreaming, and they treated him with **contempt**, making his life miserable. When he was fourteen, Hans **persuaded** his mother to let him go to the big city of Copenhagen, where he tried to get work as an actor, but was unsuccessful. He also tried dancing and singing, but he was not very good at these either. He tried writing plays, but they were **rejected** by theater owners. In this **phase** of his life, he didn't seem to fit in anywhere.

But Hans Christian Andersen **persisted** in his efforts to be a writer. Over the next fifteen years he wrote poems, travel articles, and novels, as well as plays. He worked very hard, taking care to **revise** each sentence carefully until he got the words just right. No one paid much attention to his work, however, until he began writing fairy tales. He did not have to search for ideas for these; all he had to do was **recall** the stories his father had told him when he was a little boy. He wrote more than a hundred and fifty wonderful fairy tales, at last **achieving** fame and becoming one of the best-loved writers in the world. You will read one of his stories in the next lesson.

Answer each of the following questions in the form of a sentence. If a question does not contain a vocabulary word from this lesson's word list, use one in your answer. Use each word only once. Questions and answers will then contain all fifteen words (or forms of the words).

1. How do you think a **sensitive** person like Andersen might have responded to cruel remarks?

He could get very offended and upset

2. What was one of Andersen's favorite childhood activities?

His theatrical world of his own plays

3. Why did the people in Hans's toy theater look so charmingly old-fashioned?

They dressed quaint in Denmark.

4. What caused an **abrupt** change in Andersen's life when he was a child?

His dad died.

5. What might Andersen have said to **persuade** his mother to let him go to Copenhagen?

He said he did not fit in life.

6. Why must Andersen's mother have been pessimistic about his chances of success?

He failed every job he attempted.

7. How do you know that Andersen was not popular with his fellow workers?

Everyone mocked him.

8. Was Andersen's playwriting successful?

His playwriting was rejected.

9. What jobs did Hans try during the **phase** of his life when he didn't fit in anywhere?

He danced, sing, act and wrote plays.

10. In your opinion, what was Andersen's greatest **achievement**?

He was a famous for writing books.

11. What helped give Andersen ideas for stories?

He recalled his stories from his childhood.

12. How can you tell that Andersen was usually not satisfied with his first version of a story?

He felt contempted with his story.

13. What quality did Andersen have that helped him succeed?

He was being persistent.

14. Why do you think the people Andersen worked with mocked him?

He never was successful with any job.

15. Why might the story of the Ugly Duckling be of special interest to Andersen's readers?

It is intresting because it might give a quick glimpse about his life.

FUN & FASCINATING FACTS

The Latin *abruptus* means "broken" and forms the root of the adjective **abrupt**. If there is an *abrupt* end to something—a speech, for example—it means it was *broken* off suddenly and unexpectedly.

Other words formed from this root include *interrupt* (When you *interrupt* a conversation, you *break* into it) and *disrupt* (If you *disrupt* a meeting, you *break* it up).

Lesson 6

Word List
Study the definitions of the words below; then do the exercises for the lesson.

applaud
ə plôd´

v. 1. To show approval, especially by clapping hands.
The audience **applauded** until the actors came back on stage to take another bow.
applause *n.* The showing of approval or enjoyment by cheering or clapping.
The theater lights came on after the **applause** had died down.

crafty
krafv tē

adj. Skilled at tricking others.
Templeton, the **crafty** and mean-spirited rat in *Charlotte's Web*, adds humor to the book.

disclose
dis klōz´

v. 1. To make known.
The judge told the reporter she must **disclose** the names of those who attended the meeting.

drab
drab

adj. Dull and without color; not cheerful or colorful.
A sparrow is a **drab** little bird compared to a male cardinal.

entire
en tīr´

adj. Having nothing left out; whole; complete.
I recited the **entire** Robert Frost poem from memory.

exclaim
eks klām´

v. To speak suddenly and with strong feeling.
"Today was the worst day of my life!" she exclaimed.
exclamation (eks klə mā´ shən) *n.* A sharp cry of strong feeling.
Grandpa's **exclamation** of pain sent me rushing to his side.

exquisite
ek skwiz´ it

adj. Finely done or made; very beautiful.
The **exquisite** wood carvings on the museum door came from the island of Bali.

intend
in tend´

v. To plan; to have in mind.
I **intend** to give a piano recital on Monday.
intention *n.* An aim, plan, or purpose.
It was Thea's **intention** to open a bookstore, but she decided to go to engineering school instead.

jeer
jir

v. To speak or cry out in scorn; to mock.
My brother told me to ignore them if the older boys **jeered** when I sang.
n. Something said that is meant to hurt or insult.
An umpire soon learns to ignore the **jeers** of the crowd.

peer
pir

v. To look closely; to stare, especially at something that is hard to see or to understand.
Ahmed **peered** at the sign, trying to read what it said.

progress
prä´ grəs

n. 1. Moving toward a goal.
The stormy sea slowed the small boat's **progress.**
2. An improvement.
I am finally making some **progress** mastering the new computer program.

v. (prə gres´) 1. To move forward.
Work on the new bridge **progressed** at a faster pace when the weather improved.
2. To advance to a higher stage; to improve.
Manuel **progressed** so fast on the tuba that he got into the school band.

refine
ri fīn´

v. To make pure by removing all unwanted matter.
We take oil from deep inside the earth and **refine** it into gasoline.
refined   *adj.* 1. In a pure state.
When flour is **refined**, a lot of the wheat germ is lost.
2. Having good manners and good taste.
He was a noisy and rude boy, but as young man he is gentle and **refined**.

scoundrel
skoun´ drəl

n. A mean or wicked person.
Thank heavens the police caught the **scoundrel** who stole my wallet.

uneasy
un ē´ zē

adj. Not comfortable; worried or nervous.
I felt **uneasy** walking down the dark street until I observed a police officer on the corner.

vain
vān

adj. 1. Having too high an opinion of one's looks or achievements.
Charlie is so **vain** he has a full-length mirror in every room.
2. Without success.
The firefighters made a **vain** attempt to keep the fire from spreading.
in vain   *adv.* Without success or result; useless.
All my hand-waving was **in vain**—the teacher never called on me.

6A Finding Meanings

Choose two phrases to form a sentence that correctly uses a word from Word List 6. Write each sentence in the space provided.

1. (a) one that is complete.   (c) one that is not broken.
   (b) An entire set is   (d) An exquisite set is

An exquisite set is one that is complete.

2. (a) Crafty persons are those who   (c) Vain persons are those who
   (b) think too highly of themselves.   (d) do not think well of themselves.

Vain persons are those who think too highly of themselves.

3. (a) beautiful to look at.   (c) An exquisite fabric is one that is
   (b) A drab fabric is one that is   (d) hidden from view.

An exquisite fabric is one that is beautiful to look at.

4. (a) A jeer is   (c) a small hand tool.
   (b) A scoundrel is   (d) a dishonest person.

A scoundrel is a dishonest person.

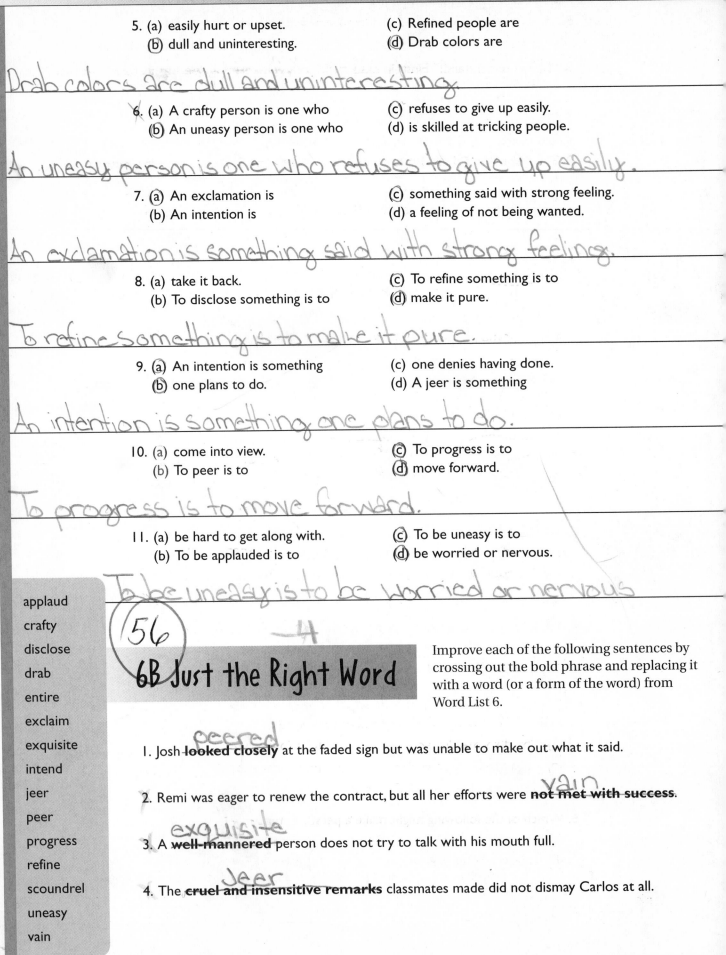

5. (a) easily hurt or upset.
   (b) dull and uninteresting.
   (c) Refined people are
   (d) Drab colors are

Drab colors are dull and uninteresting.

6. (a) A crafty person is one who
   (b) An uneasy person is one who
   (c) refuses to give up easily.
   (d) is skilled at tricking people.

An uneasy person is one who refuses to give up easily.

7. (a) An exclamation is
   (b) An intention is
   (c) something said with strong feeling.
   (d) a feeling of not being wanted.

An exclamation is something said with strong feeling.

8. (a) take it back.
   (b) To disclose something is to
   (c) To refine something is to
   (d) make it pure.

To refine something is to make it pure.

9. (a) An intention is something
   (b) one plans to do.
   (c) one denies having done.
   (d) A jeer is something

An intention is something one plans to do.

10. (a) come into view.
    (b) To peer is to
    (c) To progress is to
    (d) move forward.

To progress is to move forward.

11. (a) be hard to get along with.
    (b) To be applauded is to
    (c) To be uneasy is to
    (d) be worried or nervous.

To be uneasy is to be worried or nervous

(56)   −4

applaud
crafty
disclose
drab
entire
exclaim
exquisite
intend
jeer
peer
progress
refine
scoundrel
uneasy
vain

6B Just the Right Word

Improve each of the following sentences by crossing out the bold phrase and replacing it with a word (or a form of the word) from Word List 6.

1. Josh **looked closely** *peered* at the faded sign but was unable to make out what it said.

2. Remi was eager to renew the contract, but all her efforts were **not met with success** *vain*.

3. A **well-mannered** *exquisite* person does not try to talk with his mouth full.

4. The **cruel and insensitive remarks** *jeer* classmates made did not dismay Carlos at all.

5. Icy road conditions slowed our ~~forward movement~~ *progress* through town.

6. "Now I understand!" Einstein **~~said suddenly, with strong feeling~~** *exclaimed*, as he jumped up.

7. He was so **~~good at tricking people~~** *crafty* that those he fooled did not even know it.

8. The inspector did not **let anyone know** the reason for her visit to the factory.

9. There was loud ~~cheering and clapping~~ *applaud* when the members of the band came on stage.

6C Applying Meanings

Circle the letter of each correct answer to the questions below. A question may have more than one correct answer.

1. Which of the following might look **drab**?
   - (a) a dark suit of clothes
   - (b) a rainbow
   - (c) a freshly painted room
   - (d) a circus clown

2. Which of the following are **entire** words?
   - (a) father
   - (b) m th r
   - (c) s me b dy
   - (d) I

3. Which of the following might be called **exquisite**?
   - (a) a wedding dress
   - (b) a diamond necklace
   - (c) a grease spot
   - (d) a trash can

4. What might cause **jeers** from the crowd at a baseball game?
   - (a) an umpire's bad call
   - (b) a win for the home team
   - (c) a home run
   - (d) a dropped catch

5. Which of the following might someone **peer** at?
   - (a) a hard-to-read letter
   - (b) a quaintly dressed person
   - (c) a loud noise
   - (d) an unpleasant smell

6. Which of the following might make a person **uneasy**?
   - (a) winning first prize
   - (b) hearing strange noises
   - (c) climbing a tall ladder
   - (d) being left alone at night

7. Which of the following would it be **vain** to attempt?

~~(a)~~ unscrambling an egg   (c) traveling backward in time

~~(b)~~ learning Chinese   ~~(d)~~ climbing Mount Everest

8. Which of the following would a person be likely to **applaud**?

(a) a great achievement   (c) an entertaining show

(b) a pessimistic remark   (d) a patriotic speech

6D Word Study

Look at the words below. Circle the two words in each group of four that are synonyms.

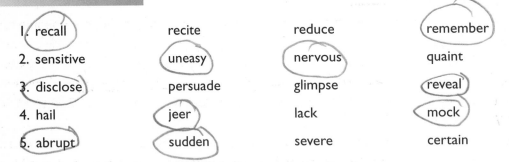

1. (recall)	recite	reduce	(remember)
2. sensitive	(uneasy)	(nervous)	quaint
3. (disclose)	persuade	glimpse	(reveal)
4. hail	(jeer)	lack	(mock)
5. (abrupt)	(sudden)	severe	certain

Look at the words below. Circle the two words in each group of four that are antonyms.

6. complete	vain	(modest)	(sufficient)
7. excessive	(exquisite)	(drab)	forbidden
8. drowsy	(crafty)	(foolish)	destructive
9. (ease)	(contempt)	respect	preparation
10. disclose	(applaud)	intend	(jeer)

applaud
crafty
disclose
drab
entire
exclaim
exquisite
intend
jeer
peer
progress
refine
scoundrel
uneasy
vain

6E Passage

Read the passage below; then complete the exercise that follows.

The Emperor's New Clothes*

Once there was an emperor who was very **vain**, spending hour after hour **peering** at himself in the mirror. Whenever he got new clothes he would gather his ministers around him so that they could tell him how wonderful he looked.

One day, two men who said they were master tailors came to see the emperor. They told him they could make him a suit of clothes so magnificent that everything else he owned would seem **drab**. The cloth would be so unusual that only those with the most **refined** taste would be able to see it. The emperor was foolish enough to believe them and agreed to pay whatever they asked.

*This passage is a retelling of the popular fairy tale by Hans Christian Andersen.

The "tailors" started work at once. Every day the emperor sent his ministers to check on their **progress**. Of course, they could see perfectly well that the **crafty** pair were only pretending to weave the cloth and cut it and stitch it, but they didn't dare **disclose** the truth to the emperor. The ministers were afraid to disagree with the emperor because that would be like confessing that they did not have good taste. They felt **uneasy** about lying, but they believed they had no choice. They told the emperor only what he wanted to hear—that his new clothes were the most **exquisite** they had ever seen.

When the two **scoundrels** told the emperor that their work was complete, he was so excited that he announced that the next day would be a public holiday. He **intended** to walk through the streets of the town in his new clothes so that everyone could admire him. The next morning, the "tailors" carefully laid out the emperor's new clothes and began helping him dress. The ministers gathered around to watch, and there were loud **exclamations** of delight when the emperor, turning this way and that, at last stood proudly before them dressed only in his underwear.

Officers of the palace guard had been up since before dawn making sure that the townspeople turned out to **applaud** the emperor as he went by. The **entire** town lined the streets to see him. Under the watchful eyes of the officers, the people cheered and waved flags, and the emperor loved every minute of it. But then something unexpected happened. Above the roar of the crowd, the emperor heard a child's voice saying, "Look! The emperor has no clothes!" The cry was at once taken up by the crowd. "THE EMPEROR HAS NO CLOTHES! THE EMPEROR HAS NO CLOTHES!"

The emperor looked down at himself and saw that it was true. He knew that he had been tricked. Feeling very foolish, he ran back to the palace as fast as he could, the **jeers** of the crowd ringing in his ears.

Answer each of the following questions in the form of a sentence. If a question does not contain a vocabulary word from this lesson's word list, use one in your answer. Use each word only once. Questions and answers will then contain all fifteen words (or forms of the words).

1. What did the emperor do with his time?

He spend time looking at him self when got new cloths

2. Why might the emperor have been tempted to get rid of all his old clothes after he talked to his tailors?

The other clothes he owned would look drab

3. How would you describe **refined** taste?

Pure taste

4. Why was it impossible to judge how the tailors' work was **progressing**?

They were acting crafty so they couldn't judge

5. Why does the passage refer to the two tailors as **scoundrels**?

They made no clothes.

6. Who finally **disclosed** the truth to the emperor?

A child yelled the truth.

7. Why were the ministers **uneasy**?

They were worried and thought the tailors were scoundrels.

8. What did the ministers tell the emperor?

The tailors were scoundrels.

9. What do you think the ministers thought of the two tailors?

They had a intend in there mind.

10. What do you think was the tailors' **intention** in tricking the emperor?

Getting more money by doing stuff.

11. Why did the ministers **exclaim** in delight?

The emperor was not wearing anything

12. Why do you think the child might have deserved the crowd's **applause**?

He told the truth.

13. Why did the **entire** town show up to see the emperor?

They wanted to see what was happening.

14. Why did the emperor run back to the palace?

Everyone jeered him.

15. What vocabulary word describes the emperor perfectly? Why?

exquisite because it means it was finely done or made.

FUN & FASCINATING FACTS

The adjective **drab** is also the name of a color —a light, green-brown. (U.S. soldiers wear olive-*drab* clothing.) *Drab* is also a noun meaning "a small amount," but it is found only in the phrase "in dribs and drabs," meaning a little bit at a time. (Instead of paying me the money all at once, they gave it to me *in dribs and drabs*.)

As well as being a verb, **peer** is also a noun. It means "an equal; a person of the same rank or position as another." For example, "Those sixth graders are my *peers*. We all are in the same class." Or, to say that Daniel Webster had no *peer* as a public speaker is to say that no one could equal him in the art of public speaking. A *peer* is also the name for a member of the British House of Lords.

Note that **peer** and *pier* are homophones, words that sound alike but have different meanings and spellings.

Vain and *vein* are another pair of homophones. A *vein* is a blood vessel that carries blood to the heart.

Lesson 7

> **Word List** Study the definitions of the words below; then do the exercises for the lesson.

alter
ôl´ tər

v. To change in some way; to make or become different.
Let's **alter** our uniforms so they will fit better.
alteration *n.* A change.
Please don't make any **alterations** in my newspaper column.

confuse
kən fyo͞oz´

v. 1. To make or become unclear or mixed up in the mind.
That math problem totally **confused** me.
2. To mistake one person or thing for another.
I always **confuse** Sally with her twin sister Samantha.
confusing *adj.* Hard to follow or understand; unclear.
The play was **confusing** at first, but I began to understand it in the second act.
confusion *n.* A state of disorder.
After the playoff game, the dressing room was total **confusion**.

distribute
di strib´ yo͞ot

v. 1. To give out; to divide among several or many.
Ahmed **distributed** programs before the concert.
2. To be spread over.
Small parks are **distributed** throughout London.

eject
i jekt´

v. To force or throw out.
When the seventh graders refused to listen, the coach **ejected** them from the team meeting.

embrace
im brās´

v. 1. To hold closely in one's arms; to hug.
My parents **embraced** me when I got off the plane.
2. To take up seriously.
We **embraced** the idea of smaller classes, but lacked the teachers to carry it out.
n. A hug.
At the end of the movie, the hero and the heroine were locked in an **embrace**.

equip
i kwip´

v. To provide with what is needed.
All new cars now come **equipped** with airbags.
equipment *n.* Things that are needed for some activity.
Sarah bought all her camping **equipment** at yard sales.

flexible
flek´ sə bəl

adj. 1. Able to bend easily.
Dancers and gymnasts have very **flexible** bodies.
2. Able to adjust to new or different situations.
Antonio is so **flexible** he can get along with anyone.

instant
in´ stənt

n. A moment; a very short period of time.
It took Luis only an **instant** to calculate the amount of paint we would need.
adj. Happening or done at once; quick.
He gave an **instant** "yes" to her offer.

keen kēn	*adj.* 1. Having a sharp edge. The **keen** blade of the knife sliced through the thick rope with ease. 2. Showing a strong interest; eager. Marta signed up for lessons because she was **keen** to learn to play the guitar. 3. Having sharp senses; quick to understand. With her **keen** mind, she was able to master physics with ease.
limp limp	*v.* To walk lamely or in an uneven way. I **limped** for two weeks after I fell on the ice. *n.* An uneven or lopsided walk. She walked very fast, in spite of her **limp**. *adj.* Not stiff or firm. His handshake was as **limp** as a wet rag.
scurry skur´ ē	*v.* To move quickly, with rapid little steps. The chipmunk **scurried** up the tree as we approached.
seize sēz	*v.* 1. To grasp suddenly; to grab hold of. He **seized** my hand and begged me not to go. 2. To take by force of the law. The government can **seize** many of the things you own if you do not pay your taxes.
shallow sha´ lō	*adj.* 1. Not deep. We went wading in a **shallow** stream. 2. With little seriousness or deep thought. He tried to sound intelligent, but his arguments were really quite **shallow**.
surround sə round´	*v.* To enclose on all sides. The prison was **surrounded** by a high fence. **surroundings** *n. pl.* The things or conditions around a person or place. The hotel's peaceful **surroundings** made it a perfect place to relax.
victim vik´ təm	*n.* One who is hurt, killed, or suffers. The scoundrel tried to deny that he had cheated his **victims** of their life savings.

7A Finding Meanings

Choose two phrases to form a sentence that correctly uses a word from Word List 7. Write each sentence in the space provided.

100

1. (a) Surroundings are
   (b) Alterations are
   (c) needed items for some activity.
   (d) the conditions around one.

Surroundings are the conditions around one.

2. (a) To eject a group is to
   (b) provide it with what is needed.
   (c) To equip a group is to
   (d) allow it to take part.

To equip a group is to provide it with what is needed.

3. (a) throw them out.   (c) take them by force.
   (b) To seize papers is to   (d) To distribute papers is to

To sieze papers is to take them by force.

4. (a) To be flexible is to be   (c) unwilling to change your mind.
   (b) To be keen is to be   (d) agreeable to any sudden change of plan.

To be flexible is to be agreeable to any sudden change.

5. (a) Alteration is   (c) a state of being mixed up.
   (b) unwillingness to change.   (d) Confusion is

Confusion is a state of being mixed up.

6. (a) Victims are   (c) persons who avoid injury.
   (b) persons who are hurt.   (d) Embraces are

Victims are persons who are hurt.

7. (a) A flexible person   (c) A keen person
   (b) is one who is eager.   (d) is one who is vain.

A keen person is one who is eager.

8. (a) a hug.   (c) An instant is
   (b) An embrace is   (d) a handshake.

An embrace is a hug.

9. (a) To limp is to   (c) To scurry is to
   (b) grasp firmly.   (d) walk unevenly.

To limp is to walk unevenly.

10. (a) to hold onto them.   (c) To distribute things is
    (b) to give them out.   (d) To confuse things is

To distribute things is to give them out

alter
confuse
distribute
eject
embrace
equip
flexible
instant
keen
limp
scurry
seize
shallow
surround
victim

7B Just the Right Word

Improve each of the following sentences by crossing out the bold phrase and replacing it with a word (or a form of the word) from Word List 7.

1. The dog's **uneven walk** ~~limp~~ was caused by a thorn in its left front paw.

2. I **opened my arms and held** ~~embraced~~ my cousin, whom I hadn't seen in two years.

3. Stay close to shore where the water is **not very deep** ~~shallow~~.

4. My cat jumped as a mouse ran with quick little steps *scurried* across the kitchen floor.

5. I caught a glimpse of the president in the parade for just a(n) very short period of time *instant*.

6. This map is very hard to follow *confusing* because some of the streets aren't named.

7. With just a slight change in form *alter* of the shape of the number, a 3 becomes an 8.

8. The boxes of food were given out *distributed* in time for Thanksgiving.

9. My whole family gathered around *surrounded* me, singing "Happy Birthday."

10. Luckily, the pilot was thrown with great force *ejected* from the plane before it crashed.

7C Applying Meanings

Circle the letter of each correct answer to the questions below. A question may have more than one correct answer.

1. Which of the following can be **altered**?
   - (a) one's plans
   - (b) today's date
   - (c) a dress's hemline
   - (d) one's age

2. Which of the following are **flexible**?
   - (a) a sewing needle
   - (b) a garden hose
   - (c) a dancer's body
   - (d) a length of cooked spaghetti

3. Which of the following could be given in an **instant**?
   - (a) a yes-or-no answer
   - (b) a nod of agreement
   - (c) a ten-page report
   - (d) a smile of welcome

4. Which of the following might feel **limp**?
   - (a) a sheet of wet cardboard
   - (b) a sleeping child
   - (c) a sheet of ice
   - (d) a sheet of plywood

5. Which of the following could **scurry**?
   - (a) a spider
   - (b) a whale
   - (c) an elephant
   - (d) a mouse

6. Which of the following could be **seized**?

   (a) a person's arm

   (b) a person's boat

   (c) a sneeze

   (d) a puff of smoke

7. Which of the following could be **shallow**?

   (a) a stick

   (b) a tree

   (c) a person's thinking

   (d) a pond

8. Which of the following might be **keen**?

   (a) a pessimist

   (b) a razor blade

   (c) a hammer

   (d) a dog's hearing

7D Word Study

In Lesson 5, you met three prefixes, *un-*, *in-*, and *im-*. When attached to the front of a word, they turned the word into its opposite. The meaning of each prefix is "not."

Here are three more prefixes. They add to, or change the meaning of, the word they're attached to. *Pre-* adds the meaning "before," *re-* adds the meaning "again" or "against," and *ex-* adds the meaning "out." The prefix *ex-* is sometimes shortened to *e-*.

In column three, write the prefix of each word listed in column two. In column four, write the meaning of each prefix.

Definition	Word	Prefix	Prefix Meaning
1. to fight against	resist	_____	_____
2. to bring out into the open	expose	_____	_____
3. to act before the need arises	prepare	_____	_____
4. not feeling easy in one's mind	uneasy	_____	_____
5. to bring to mind once again	recall	_____	_____
6. to go out of bounds	exceed	_____	_____
7. to go over to correct	revise	_____	_____
8. to speak out loudly	exclaim	_____	_____
9. to throw out	eject	_____	_____
10. to say over again what one has memorized	recite	_____	_____

alter

confuse

distribute

eject

embrace

equip

flexible

instant

keen

limp

scurry

seize

shallow

surround

victim

7E Passage

Read the passage below; then complete the exercise that follows.

Armed but Not Dangerous

What is sometimes green, sometimes brown, sometimes gray, sometimes a mixture of all three colors, and has one head and eight arms? Here is a clue: the Greek word for eight is *okto*. If you guessed octopus, you're right!

The octopus lives in holes or openings in the rocky bottom of the sea, where it protects itself from its enemies by changing its color to match its **surroundings**. In seaweed it can turn green; on sand it can turn brown; against rocks it can turn gray. For example, if it is attacked by a shark, it can change its color in an **instant** in order to blend into the background. The surprised shark is left wondering where the octopus went. It can also protect itself by **ejecting** a large blob of black ink-like liquid that acts as a screen. This **confuses** its attacker, who may go after the dark blob, giving the octopus a chance to escape.

An octopus has no bones, so it can easily **alter** its shape; it can then force its way inside empty shells or under rocks or into very narrow openings. To be even safer, it may cover itself with stones or shells.

The octopus's eight rubbery arms are very **flexible** and can easily be wrapped around even quite small objects. Each arm is **equipped** with two rows of fleshy, deeply set suckers that give it a powerful grip. The octopus uses its arms to **seize** other animals such as crabs and lobsters as they **scurry** along the sea floor. It can then use the two strong, horny beaks in its mouth to crack open the shell of its **victim**.

The octopus has **keen** eyesight, which it needs because it hunts mostly at night. It has a large brain for its size, and it makes full use of its intelligence in its efforts to catch food. For example, if an octopus cannot open a clam, it will wait until the clam opens itself. When it does, the octopus will put a stone between the two shells so that they cannot close. Then it can get at the juicy clam without having to struggle.

There are many different kinds of octopuses, and they are widely **distributed** throughout the world's oceans. They live mostly in warm, **shallow** water, not far from shore. The smallest ones grow to be no more than two inches across; the largest ones, which live in the Pacific Ocean, can grow to be thirty feet across, although their bodies might be only eighteen inches.

If, when swimming in the Pacific, you venture too far from shore, you may find yourself in the **embrace** of one of these creatures. If this should happen to you, it is best not to struggle. If you let your body go **limp**, the octopus will probably let you go. Although movies sometimes show them as terrifying and dangerous monsters, there is no reason to fear them. Around humans, at least, octopuses are usually shy and gentle creatures.

Answer each of the following questions in the form of a sentence. If a question does not contain a vocabulary word from this lesson's word list, use one in your answer. Use each word only once. Questions and answers will then contain all fifteen words (or forms of the words).

1. Why does an octopus sitting in seaweed turn green?

2. How long does it take for an octopus to change colors?

3. Why does the octopus make a "screen"?

4. How does it make this screen?

5. How does its lack of a skeleton benefit an octopus?

6. How would bones in an octopus's arms affect the way it uses them?

7. How is the octopus **equipped** to grip things?

8. How do its eight arms help an octopus obtain food?

9. Why might an approaching octopus cause a crab to start **scurrying**?

10. How does an octopus get at the meat in a lobster it has caught?

11. Which of the octopus's senses is especially well-developed?

12. In what parts of the world do octopuses live?

13. Why are you unlikely to see an octopus in the middle of the Atlantic Ocean?

14. Would you be in danger in an octopus's **embrace**? Explain.

15. What is the meaning of **limp**, as used in the passage?

FUN & FASCINATING FACTS

Alter is a verb; *altar* (with two *a*'s) is a noun. An *altar* is a table or platform used in churches or temples as a center of worship. A bride and groom may kneel or stand before the altar when they get married. *Alter* and *altar* are homophones—words that sound alike but have different meanings and spellings.

Flexible means "able to bend or change easily." The antonym of *flexible* is *rigid,* which means "stiff" or "unbending." An iron bar is rigid; if it is heated until it becomes red- or white-hot, it becomes flexible. Both words can be used *literally,* as in the example above, and *figuratively*, as in the examples below. A person who is willing to change plans at the last minute is said to be *flexible*, whereas someone who refuses to make such changes could be called *rigid.* A job with *rigid* hours is one in which the hours of work cannot be changed; a job with *flexible* hours is one in which the hours can be changed easily to suit the needs of the worker or the boss.

Lesson 8

Word List
Study the definitions of the words below; then do the exercises for the lesson.

ancient
ān´ chənt

adj. Very old; of a long time ago.
The **ancient** city of Carthage was destroyed by the Romans in 146 B.C.

century
sen´ chər ē

n. A period of one hundred years.
The twenty-first **century** began on January 1, 2001.

chamber
chām´ bər

n. A room.
Chamber music is meant to be played in a room rather than a much larger concert hall.
chambers *n. pl.* An office or group of offices.
Lawyers for both sides met in the judge's **chambers**.

descend
di send´

v. To go or come down.
The plane slowly **descended** to 2,000 feet.
descendant *n.* One who has certain persons as one's parents, grandparents, etc.
The writer Alex Haley was a **descendant** of Kunta Kinte, who was brought to America as a slave from West Africa in 1767.

entry
en´ trē

n. 1. A way in.
The thieves gained **entry** through an unlocked window.
2. Each separate item in a diary or list.
The next **entry** in her diary simply said, "My brother returned home today after a long absence."

interior
in tir´ ē ər

n. The inside part of something.
The sun's **interior** is about 150,000 times hotter than boiling water.
adj. Having to do with the inside part.
Interior doors do not have to be as strongly made as front or back doors.

intrude
in trōōd´

v. To come or go in without permission or welcome.
I didn't mean to **intrude** on you while you were working.
intrusion *n.* The act of intruding.
"Forgive my **intrusion**," she said as she came in without knocking.
intruder *n.* One who intrudes.
People were so unfriendly that I felt like an **intruder** at Jeff's party.

locate
lō´ kāt

v. 1. To find.
Marta **located** the missing books in less than an hour.
2. To put or to be found in a place.
We're going to **locate** our office across the street from the school.
location (lō´ kā´ shən) *n.* The place where something can be found.
Will you please give me the **location** of the nearest post office?

passage
paˊ sij

n. 1. A part of a written work or piece of music.
The final **passage** of the Mozart mass brought tears to the audience's eyes.
2. The act or process of passing, as through time or from place to place.
His deeply lined face clearly showed the **passage** of time.
3. A way through which to pass.
Leon's room was at the end of a long, dimly lit **passage**.

portion
pôrˊ shən

n. 1. A part or share of the whole.
I got the first **portion** of my allowance last week.
2. A serving or helping, as of food.
My diet recommends a four-ounce **portion** of fish or chicken once a day.

precious
preˊ shəs

adj. 1. Very valuable.
The necklace was made of diamonds, emeralds, and other **precious** stones.
2. Much loved.
She tried in vain to save her **precious** books from the fire.

quarry
kwôrˊ ē

n. 1. A deep pit where stone is cut out of the ground.
The marble for these tiles came from a **quarry** in Vermont.
2. An animal that is being hunted.
The hunters gave up the chase when they lost sight of their **quarry**.

ramp
ramp

n. A slanted walk or roadway that connects a lower to a higher place.
The law says that there has to be a **ramp** for those who cannot use the steps.

spacious
spāˊ shəs

adj. Having lots of room.
The **spacious** kitchen had room for a large round table that seated eight.

surface
sʉrˊ fəs

n. 1. The outside layer; the top.
The **surface** of the moon is covered with craters.
2. An outward look or appearance.
He seemed cheerful on the **surface**, but I knew how miserable he must have felt to be so cold and wet.
v. To rise to the top of a body of water.
The latest submarines can stay underwater for weeks before they need to **surface**.

8A Finding Meanings

Choose two phrases to form a sentence that correctly uses a word from Word List 8. Write each sentence in the space provided.

1. (a) Interior walls are
   (b) those on the inside.
   (c) those that surround a private area.
   (d) Ancient walls are

Interior walls are those on the inside.

2. (a) The passage of something is
   (b) The surface of something is
   (c) its outward appearance.
   (d) its innermost part.

The surface of something is its outward appearance.

3. (a) A spacious city is one   (c) that is very old.
   (b) that has many visitors.   (d) An ancient city is one

An ancient city is one that is very old.

4. (a) A passage is   (c) An intrusion is
   (b) a free pass to a public event.   (d) a way through which to go.

A passage is a way through wich to go.

5. (a) Something that is spacious   (c) is very valuable.
   (b) Something that is precious   (d) seems true but is actually false.

Something that is precious is very valuable

6. (a) a sloping walkway.   (c) A ramp is
   (b) A quarry is   (d) a contest.

A ramp is a sloping walkway

7. (a) an unwelcome arrival.   (c) A location is
   (b) a serving of food.   (d) An intrusion is

An intrusion is an unwelcome arrival

8. (a) A portion is   (c) a pit from which stone is cut.
   (b) A quarry is   (d) a building open to the public.

A quarry is a pit from wich stone is cut.

9. (a) To locate the stairs is   (c) to go up them.
   (b) to go down them.   (d) To descend the stairs is

To descend the stairs is to go down them.

10. (a) A portion is   (c) a large room.
    (b) A chamber is   (d) the topmost part.

A chamber is a large room.

ancient
century
chamber
descend
entry
interior
intrude
locate
passage
portion
precious
quarry
ramp
spacious
surface

8B Just the Right Word

Improve each of the following sentences by crossing out the bold phrase and replacing it with a word (or a form of the word) from Word List 8.

1. Our new apartment has a closet that is ~~very large,~~ *spacious* with room enough to hold a fold-up bed.

2. The United States has enough coal to last for at least a ~~period of one hundred years.~~ *century*

3. The divers were searching for the ~~exact spot~~ *location* of the sunken treasure.

4. To enter the parking garage you have to drive up the **sloping way** *ramp* leading to a higher level.

5. The lion's **intended victim** *intrusion* was a young antelope.

6. As we approached the clubhouse, we saw that the only **way in** *entry* was blocked by a huge pile of snow.

7. Angela told me she would pay back a **part of the total amount** *portion* of the money she owed me by next week.

8. These are the **group of offices** *chambers* where Senate hearings are held.

9. The **process of passing** *passage* of time could be seen in the crumbling stone buildings and rutted streets.

10. A large bullfrog suddenly **rose to the top of the water** *descended* and landed on a lilypad.

8C Applying Meanings

Circle the letter of each correct answer to the questions below. A question may have more than one correct answer.

1. Which of the following might be thought of as **precious**?
   (a) a child
   (b) freedom of speech
   (c) a diamond ring
   (d) chewing gum stuck to your shoe

2. Which of the following is **ancient**?
   (a) a joke you've heard before
   (b) last year's calendar
   (c) an Egyptian mummy
   (d) a dinosaur bone

3. Which of the following might an **intruder** at a private meeting be asked to do?
   (a) help give out the notes
   (b) join in the talk
   (c) leave immediately
   (d) meet the other people

4. Which of the following might a person try to **locate**?
   (a) a problem with a car's engine
   (b) the city of New York on a map
   (c) a missing relative
   (d) a secret

5. Which of the following might you ask for a **portion** of?
   (a) a friend's jacket
   (b) the Sunday newspaper
   (c) cole slaw
   (d) a friend's age

6. Which of the following has an **interior**?
   - (a) a planet
   - (c) a house
   - (b) a sheet of paper
   - (d) a car

7. Which of the following can be measured in **centuries**?
   - (a) the age of the United States
   - (c) time
   - (b) the size of the United States
   - (d) space

8. Which of the following has a **surface**?
   - (a) a sharp pain
   - (c) a lake
   - (b) a coat of paint
   - (d) the sun

8D Word Study

Write the synonym of each word on the left on the line next to it. Choose from the words on the right, which are in a different order.

0

1. spacious   _precious_   valuable
2. precious   _ancient_   old
3. keen   _seize_   grasp
4. ancient   _progress_   improve
5. applaud   _alter_   change
6. locate   _keen_   eager
7. alter   _spacious_   roomy
8. seize   _embrace_   hug
9. embrace   _applaud_   cheer
10. progress   _locate_   find

ancient

century

chamber

descend

entry

interior

intrude

locate

passage

portion

precious

quarry

ramp

spacious

surface

8E Passage

Read the passage below; then complete the exercise that follows.

The Great Pyramid

Over two thousand years ago, a Greek writer named Antipater made a list of what he called the Seven Wonders of the World. The only one of those **ancient** sights that remains today is the Great Pyramid, in Egypt.

The Great Pyramid is **located** just outside Cairo. It was built by one of the earliest kings of Egypt, who intended it to be a tomb, or burial place, for himself. Covering an area bigger than one hundred football fields and standing 450 feet high, it is the largest of the more than sixty pyramids in Egypt. It is made of two and a half million blocks of stone, some of which weigh as much as fifteen tons. Its **surface** was once covered in shining white limestone and was perfectly smooth, but over the **centuries** most of this has been stripped away and very little of it is left.

It may have taken as long as twenty years to build the Great Pyramid. The stone came from nearby, while the white limestone on the outside came from **quarries** near the Nile River. The blocks were floated across on rafts and were then dragged up a **ramp** of earth that was built up in stages as the work progressed. Skilled stonecutters worked all year on the pyramid. Other work was done by farmers, who worked for a **portion** of each year, probably from July to October, when the Nile overflowed its banks and flooded the fields. Workers believed that their king, Cheops, was a god, a **descendant** of the sun god Ra, and that he deserved this magnificent tomb.

The **interior** of the Great Pyramid contains many rooms, connected by **passages** leading to the outside. King Cheops was laid to rest in one of the most **spacious** rooms. The Egyptians believed in a life after death, and so they left food and drink with the king's body as well as many **precious** objects he had used in daily life. The Egyptians believed he would need these in the next world.

The **chamber** in which the dead king lay was closed off with huge granite slabs to keep people from gaining **entry** to it. In spite of this, however, **intruders** later found a way in and stole the gold objects and the jewels that were inside. They even made off with the body! The Great Pyramid failed to keep Cheops's body safe, but it has kept his name alive over 4,500 years after his death.

Answer each of the following questions in the form of a sentence. If a question does not contain a vocabulary word from this lesson's word list, use one in your answer. Use each word only once. Questions and answers will then contain all fifteen words (or forms of the words).

1. What makes the Great Pyramid unusual among the places on Antipater's list?

It's the only ancients sights that remains today.

2. How could one go from room to room within the Great Pyramid?

One can go from room to room connected by passages.

3. Why would the **interior** of the Great Pyramid be very dark?

There is not a window or light in a pyramid.

4. How did the Egyptians raise the stones onto the pyramid?

The block floated across on rafts and then dragged on a ramp.

5. Why did the white limestone have to come by water?

It came from quarries from the Nile River.

6. Why did some people work on the pyramid for only a **portion** of the year?

Farmers work for only a portion of the year the others work on the farm.

7. How does the room where the king's body was placed compare with other rooms?

The room was spacious.

8. Why do you think the passage refers to the king's room as a **chamber**?

It's called a chamber because it's a spacious room.

9. What are some of the **precious** objects that might have been left with the dead king?

Gold, jewels, and other things he owned.

10. Why did the Egyptians place granite slabs outside the king's tomb?

To keep people from gaining entry to it.

11. What happened to the gold and the jewels that were inside the tomb?

Thuders found a way to steal the gold and the jewels.

12. When (to the nearest hundred years) was the Great Pyramid built?

It was 4,500 years ago.

13. Why did the Egyptians think Cheops deserved such a magnificent tomb?

Chepos, was a god, a descendant of the sun god.

14. How does the Great Pyramid differ from when it was first built?

It is a lot bigger than it was first built

15. What is the **location** of Cairo?

The location of Cario is Egypt.

FUN & FASCINATING FACTS

In Lesson 7 you learned that the Greek word for "eight" is *okto*. In Latin, it became *octo*. (An *octopus* has eight arms. *October* was the eighth month in the Roman calendar; we changed it and made it the tenth month.)

A large number of English words are formed from Greek or Latin numbers. Among them is our word **century**, a period of one hundred years. It comes from the Latin for one hundred, which is *centum*. Other words sharing this root include *cent* (there are one hundred cents in a dollar), *centipede* (this creature was once thought to have one hundred legs, but it actually has about seventy), and *centimeter* (there are one hundred centimeters in a meter).

In 1976 the United States celebrated its *bicentennial*. If you knew nothing of the history of the United States, but knew that the Latin for "two" is *bi*, could you figure out how old the United States was in 1976?

How can the word **quarry** have two such separate and unrelated meanings? For the answer to this question, we must look into the word's history. In fact, it is not one word but two quite different ones that by chance have the same spelling.

The word for an animal being hunted comes from the old French *cuiree*, the name for body parts fed to animals after a successful hunt. The word passed into English as *querre*, which in modern English became *quarry*.

The word for a deep pit where stone is cut out of the ground comes from the Latin *quadrum*, which means "squared at the corners." It was applied to stones used for building, which were usually squared at the corners. As the word changed over time to *quarry*, it came to mean the place from which the stone was obtained.

Review for Lessons 5–8

Crossword Puzzle Solve the crossword puzzle below by studying the clues and filling in the answer boxes. Clues followed by a number are definitions of vocabulary words in Lessons 5 through 8. The number gives the lesson from which the answer to the clue is taken.

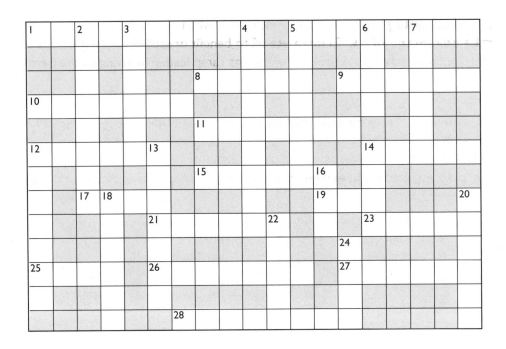

Clues Across

1. To give out (7)

5. To win over by arguing or asking (5)

8. To change in some way (7)

9. An animal that is being hunted (8)

10. The topmost part; the outer layer (8)

11. A part or share of the whole (8)

12. Twice as much

14. Each separate item on a list (8)

15. Skilled at tricking others (6)

17. Dull and without color (6)

19. Adam and _____

21. To make pure (6)

23. To take by force of the law (7)

25. Eight, _____ , ten

26. A large room (8)

27. Having nothing left out (6)

28. Place where something is (8)

Clues Down

2. To be around on all sides (7)

3. To remember (5)

4. To interest and amuse (5)

5. To go on longer than expected (5)

6. Opposite of *open*

7. Happening suddenly without warning (5)

12. To go to a lower level (8)

13. To hold closely (7)

14. Used to see with

16. Opposite of *no*

18. To say you won't accept (5)

20. Very strict or harsh

22. To throw out (7)

24. Showing a strong interest; eager (7)

Lesson 9

Word List Study the definitions of the words below; then do the exercises for the lesson.

advantage
əd van´ tij

n. Something that is helpful or useful.
It is an **advantage** to be able to speak French when visiting Paris.
take advantage of *v.* To make use of; to benefit oneself by treating others unfairly.
Martina **took advantage of** her position as camp leader by giving all the best jobs to her friends.

astonish
ə stä´ nish

v. To surprise or amaze.
It **astonished** me to discover that my new friend and I were born on the same day in the same town.
astonishment *n.* Great surprise or amazement.
The children watched in **astonishment** as the magician pulled a rabbit out of a hat.

confirm
kən fərm´

v. 1. To show or prove to be true.
Before giving me a library card, the librarian asked me to **confirm** my street address by showing a copy of my phone bill.
2. To approve or give one's agreement to.
The members of Congress vote to **confirm** the appointment of Supreme Court judges.

distant
dis´ tənt

adj. 1. Very far away in time.
Space travel in the very **distant** future may involve journeys to the stars.
2. Very far away; not near or close by.
Marco Polo's travels took him to many **distant** lands.
distance *n.* The length of the space between two places.
The **distance** between Deneen's home and her school was exactly one mile.

founder
faün´ dər

n. A person who sets up something that lasts.
George Washington and Thomas Jefferson are two of the **founders** of our nation.
v. To sink below the surface of the water.
The ship struck a rock and **foundered** before a rescue team could reach it.

hamlet
ham´ lət

n. A small village.
A single street ran through the **hamlet**, which had one church, a general store, and about a hundred houses.

host
hōst

n. 1. A large number.
Graceland is visited by **hosts** of people from all over the world who come to see the house where Elvis Presley lived.
2. One who greets and entertains guests and takes care of their needs at a party or restaurant.
The guests said goodbye to their **host** and thanked him for a lovely New Year's Eve party.

misgiving
mis giv´ ing

n. A feeling of doubt, uncertainty, or concern about what may happen in the future.
If Ellen had any **misgivings** about joining the group, she gave no sign of it.

parch pärch	v. To make or become very dry. The sun **parched** the fields and made the grass turn brown. **parched** (pärcht) adj. Lacking water; thirsty. We didn't take enough water with us, and we were **parched** before we came to the end of our walk.

prospect präs´ pekt	n. Something that is waited for, expected, or hoped for. All the hotels were full, and there seemed little **prospect** of our finding a place to spend the night. v. To look in the ground for valuable metals like gold and silver. The four men camped alongside the river told us they were **prospecting** for gold. **prospector** n. A person who explores an area to look for valuable metals. The **prospector** let out a whoop of joy when he saw some shiny yellow objects lying on the riverbank.

scarce skers	adj. In short supply; not plentiful. When gasoline is **scarce**, the price goes up. **scarcity** (sker´ sət ē) n. A shortage. Due to the **scarcity** of candles in the store when the hurricane struck, customers were allowed only two each.

shrewd shrüd	adj. Clever; good at understanding what is needed and acting on it. A **shrewd** lawyer prepares her client to answer questions she knows the client will be asked in court.

sole sōl	adj. Being the only one of its kind; belonging to only one person or group. After her husband died, Mrs. Mazoor became the **sole** owner of the toy store. n. 1. The bottom surface of the foot or of a shoe or boot. Shoes with leather **soles** usually cost more than those made of plastic. 2. A flat fish that is caught and eaten for food. Grilled **sole** is a popular item on the seafood restaurant's menu.

torment tôr´ ment	n. Great pain or suffering. I cannot imagine the **torment** suffered by a wild animal caught in a steel trap. (tôr ment´) v. To cause pain or suffering. The thought that she might have been the cause of the accident **tormented** the driver of the car.

typical tip´ i kəl	adj. Being like others of its kind. A **typical** home in this area has three bedrooms, a kitchen, a living room, and one bathroom.

9A Finding Meanings

Choose two phrases to form a sentence that correctly uses a word from Word List 9. Write each sentence in the space provided.

90

1. (a) A hamlet is
   (b) a small village.

   (c) An advantage is
   (d) a large number.

A hamlet is a small village.

2. (a) is to hurt that person.   (c) is to care for that person.
   (b) To torment someone   (d) To astonish someone

To torment someone is to hurt that person.

3. (a) A typical city   (c) is one that is far away.
   (b) is one that is very old.   (d) A distant city

A distant city is one that is far away.

4. (a) the only one of its kind.   (c) A founder is
   (b) A sole is   (d) a flat fish used for food.

A sole is the only one of its kind.

5. (a) A shrewd plan   (c) is one that is cleverly thought out.
   (b) is one that is kept secret.   (d) A typical plan

A shrewd plan is one that is cleverly thought out.

6. (a) To astonish someone   (c) To confirm someone
   (b) is to get rid of that person.   (d) is to approve that person's appointment.

To confirm someone is to approve that person's appointment.

7. (a) doubts about the future.   (c) Advantages are
   (b) unwanted gifts.   (d) Misgivings are

Misgivings are doubts about the future.

8. (a) To founder is to   (c) To prospect is to
   (b) sink below the surface.   (d) start over.

To founder is to sink below the surface.

9. (a) very thirsty.   (c) To be parched is to be
   (b) To be scarce is to be   (d) not wanted or needed.

To be parched is to be very thirsty.

10. (a) To take advantage of someone   (c) To astonish someone
    (b) is to amaze that person.   (d) is to dislike that person.

To astonish someone is to amaze that person.

−3

9B Just the Right Word

Improve each of the following sentences by crossing out the bold phrase and replacing it with a word (or a form of the word) from Word List 9.

70

1. The **length of an imaginary line going** ~~distance~~ from the earth to the moon is about a quarter of a million miles.

2. The hot sun had **taken every drop of moisture out of** the soil so that nothing grew. *parched*

3. Being tall is a(n) **extra something that can make all the difference** to a basketball player. *advantage*

4. After twenty-two miles, Asad was the **only runner as there was no other** runner left in the race. *sole*

5. Simon was very **good at knowing what to do in every situation**, and he managed to cause trouble for others without ever getting into trouble himself. *shrewd*

6. Mr. Bullwhistle is the **person who was the first owner** of this company. *founder*

7. Blankets were **in short supply and there weren't enough to go around,** so some campers got two and some got only one. *scarce*

8. Today was a(n) **example of what happens just about every** day on the island: it rained in the morning and poured in the afternoon. *prospect*

9. A **very large number** of people came together in the park to celebrate Earth Day. *host*

10. Baby Alice was busy **being cruel and causing pain to** the cat by pulling its tail. *torment*

9C Applying Meanings

Circle the letter of each correct answer to the questions below. A question may have more than one correct answer.

1. Which of the following could cause **torment**?
 (a) a bad sunburn
 (b) a broken shoelace
 (c) looking at the moon
 (d) scoring the winning goal

2. Which of the following has a **sole**?
 (a) a fish
 (b) a foot
 (c) a boot
 (d) a shoe

3. Which of the following might affect a person's **prospects** for getting into college?
 (a) red hair
 (b) leadership qualities
 (c) poor grades
 (d) ability at sports

4. Which of the following could easily be taken **advantage** of?
 (a) a weak person
 (b) a foolish person
 (c) a tall person
 (d) a small child

5. Which of the following might a **typical** American traveling abroad carry?
 (a) a camera
 (b) a guide book
 (c) a bucket
 (d) a telescope

advantage
astonish
confirm
distant
founder
hamlet
host
misgiving
parch
prospect
scarce
shrewd
sole
torment
typical

6. Which of the following might cause a **scarcity** of water?

(a) too much demand for it (c) a flood

(b) too little rain (d) thirst

7. Which of the following might cause **astonishment**?

(a) a summer snowstorm (c) a talking parrot

(b) a rainbow (d) a red apple

8. Which of the following can be **confirmed**?

(a) a sigh (c) a fact

(b) a result (d) beauty

9. Which of the following might a **host** do?

(a) welcome guests (c) show where the bathroom is

(b) give a party (d) serve food and drinks

10. For which of the following might someone go **prospecting**?

(a) air (c) gold

(b) happiness (d) jewelry

9D Word Study

In Lesson 5 you learned that words sometimes have more than one part and that there are names for these different parts. The part that comes at the beginning of a word is called a prefix. Prefixes change the meanings of words, sometimes turning them into their opposites: *un-* changes *happy* to *unhappy*.

It's time now to look at the part that forms the ending of some words. It's called a *suffix*. Suffixes have an important job also. For one thing, they change words from one part of speech to another.

Change each of the verbs below into a noun by adding the correct suffix and writing the word in the space provided. All of the words are from earlier lessons.

1. alter _alteration_

2. confuse _confusion_

3. respond _responding_

4. exclaim _exlamation_

5. intend _itended_

6. persist _persisted_

7. migrate _migration_

8. paralyze _paralyzed_

9. exceed _exceeded_

10. prepare _prepared_

11. applaud _applauding_

12. locate _location_

9E Passage

Read the passage below; then complete the exercise that follows.

The Forty-Niners

The story was in all the newspapers. It was December of 1848. Television and radio were in the **distant** future, and newspapers were the **sole** means of finding out what was going on in the world. And something was going on in California! Millions of people in homes across the United States read about it over the breakfast table. President James Polk had just **confirmed** what until then only a few people knew for certain. Gold had been discovered in California, lots of it. Now everyone knew.

A **typical** worker in the 1840s earned about a dollar a day. Gold sold for twenty dollars an ounce, and in California it was lying on the ground and in streambeds, just waiting to be picked up. Not surprisingly, thousands of Americans quit their jobs, many leaving behind their families, and headed west. If they had **misgivings**, they tried to hide them from their wives and children. The plan was to return as soon as they struck it rich. It was now 1849, and those who joined the **hosts** taking part in the California Gold Rush were called the "forty-niners."

There were no airplanes, no trains, no cars, and no roads to California in 1849. Many Easterners went there by ship. From New York, they had to go seventeen thousand miles around the tip of South America to reach San Francisco, then a **hamlet** of less than two thousand people. The journey took about six months. Those with families and lots of goods to carry traveled overland by covered wagon, which also took about six months. Crossing the Nevada desert was the worst part of the journey. Water was **scarc**e, and often the travelers would have drunk the last drop with days to go before the journey's end. They were easy victims for merchants who set out from San Francisco and traveled east to meet the **parched** travelers. These businessmen brought wagons loaded with barrels of water, which they sold—for a price! **Tormented** by thirst, travelers paid a dollar, five dollars, even a hundred dollars for a glass of the precious liquid.

Merchants like these took **advantage** of the law of supply and demand, which states that something is worth whatever someone is willing to pay for it. Sam Brannan, a San Francisco merchant and one of the city's **founders**, knew this better than anyone. The people who first discovered the gold had tried to keep it quiet, but word leaked out. Soon after Brannan heard the news, he repeated it to crowds of eager listeners and waved a jar of gold dust as proof. There was an immediate rush to buy pick axes, shovels, and the metal pans used to sift small rocks, water, and sand to look for gold. They could be bought—for a price! Before spreading the good news, Brannan had gone around the area **shrewdly** buying up every pick ax, shovel, and pan he could find. A metal pan Brannan bought for twenty cents he could now sell for fifteen dollars. And even at that price, there was no shortage of takers. In nine weeks, Brannan made thirty-six thousand dollars and went on to become the richest man in California. He was so rich he even printed his own money!

Over a quarter of a million people had poured into California by the mid-1850s. Many of the new arrivals were drawn to San Francisco, which grew at an **astonishing** rate. The price of a house went up tenfold in less than a year, and for a period of time the number of people living there doubled every ten days. Most never got rich, and many of those who did were not able to hold on to their newfound wealth. Sam Brannan was so poor when he died in 1889 that he didn't leave enough money to pay for his own burial. The forty-niners who went to California not to strike it rich by **prospecting** for gold but to work hard at ordinary jobs were the real winners. They were the ones who built California and made it what it is today—the Golden State.

advantage

astonish

confirm

distant

founder

hamlet

host

misgiving

parch

prospect

scarce

shrewd

sole

torment

typical

Answer each of the following questions in the form of a sentence. If a question does not contain a vocabulary word from this lesson's word list, use one in your answer. Use each word only once. Questions and answers will then contain all fifteen words (or forms of the words).

1. By what nickname were the **hosts** of people heading for California known?

They were called the "Forty niners."

2. How did some businessmen get rich off the suffering of **parched** travelers?

These businessmen sold wagons of water with expensive price.

3. Why do you think these businessmen took **advantage** of these travelers?

They want to get rich.

4. Why did water cost so much?

It was very scarce.

5. Did most people earn a lot of money in the 1840s?

They did not earn a lot of money

6. Describe some of the **torments** travelers in the desert suffered.

If they were thirsty they would pay 5 dollars, hundred

7. Was San Francisco a big city in the 1840s?

It was not.

8. What **misgivings** might some of the people who left their homes in the East have had?

They left there families.

9. Who was Sam Brannan?

A man who was rich and then poor

10. In what way had Sam Brannan acted **shrewdly** before spreading the news that gold had been discovered?

He sold things

11. Which well-known person **confirmed** that gold had been found in California?

James Polk president of the United States.

12. What was the **distance** between New York and California by boat?

They had to go seventeen thousand miles

13. How might you describe the growth of San Francisco between 1850 and 1855?

Over 250,000 poured in California.

14. What are people who try to find gold called?

Forty niner.

15. What was the **sole** means of finding out what was going on in California in the days before radio and television?

The newspaper

FUN & FASCINATING FACTS

Astound (Lesson 4) and **astonish** are synonyms. A third synonym, less common, is *thunderstruck*. It expresses a much greater element of surprise. If you are thunderstruck, it is almost as though you had been struck by lightning. Thunder and lightning, of course, are closely linked. *Astound, astonish*, and *thunderstruck* are also linked. Astound and astonish are formed from the Latin word *tonere*, which means "to thunder"!

In Exercise D you learned how suffixes change one part of speech to another, for example, the suffix

-ation changes the verb *alter* into the noun *alteration*. Another suffix, *-ess*, changes nouns that refer to males into nouns that refer to females. *Lion* becomes *lioness*, *actor* becomes *actress*, and **host** becomes *hostess*.

Lesson 10

Word List

Study the definitions of the words below; then do the exercises for the lesson.

ail
āl

v. To cause sickness, pain, or trouble.
"What **ails** you?" the doctor asked.
ailment   *n.* An illness; a disease.
Measles is a common childhood **ailment**.
ailing   *adj.* In poor health.
I have been **ailing** all winter.

banish
ba´ nish

v. 1. To force someone out of the country.
When the tsars ruled Russia, lawbreakers were **banished** to Siberia.
2. To get rid of completely.
Joe was such a cheerful person, he **banished** gloom wherever he went.

communicate
kə myoō´ ni kāt

v. To make known; to give or exchange information.
Since I hate to write letters, we **communicate** mostly by telephone.
communication (kə myoō ni kā´ shən) *n.* The exchange of information between people.
The misunderstanding was caused by a lack of **communication** between us.
communicative   *adj.* Willing to speak; eager to talk.
When I asked her where she had been, she was not very **communicative**, replying only, "Out."

console
kən sōl´

v. To make less sad; to comfort.
My parents tried to **console** me when my best friend moved away.
consolation (kän sə lā´ shən) *n.* Comfort.
I knew I could always turn to my aunt for **consolation** whenever I was upset.

cower
kou´ ər

v. To shrink from, as if from fear.
When I saw the poor dog **cower**, I knew its master was cruel.

deliberate
di li´ bə rət

adj. Carefully thought out; not hasty.
Although my mother was angry, she spoke in a calm and **deliberate** manner.
v. (di li´ bə rāt) To think carefully in order to make up one's mind.
We **deliberated** a long time before deciding to move to Arizona.

depth
depth

n. Distance from top to bottom or front to back; deepness.
The floodwaters reached a **depth** of several feet.
depths   *n. pl.* The innermost part or the deepest part.
The treasure chest lay buried in the **depths** of the sea.

desire
di zīr´

v. To wish for; to want very much.
A person who is famished **desires** just one thing—food!
n. A strong wish.
Pizarro's **desire** for gold was so great he ordered the Inca king, Atahualpa, to fill three rooms with it.
desirable   *adj.* Pleasing, agreeable.
My new school is in a very **desirable** location.

75

livelihood
līv´ lē hoͦod

n. The means of supporting oneself.
The storekeepers in Key West depend on tourists for their **livelihood**.

misfortune
mis fôr´ chən

n. 1. Bad luck; trouble.
He had the **misfortune** to break his leg right before the big game.
2. An unlucky event.
The 1992 hurricane was Florida's worst **misfortune** in many years.

orphan
ôr´ fən

n. A child whose parents are dead.
Tom Sawyer lived with his Aunt Polly because he was an **orphan**.

precipice
pre´ sə pəs

n. A very high and steep cliff.
We stood watchfully on the edge of the **precipice** and looked down.
precipitous (pri si´ pə təs) *adj.* 1. Very steep.
The Two-Mile Terror ski trail has many **precipitous** slopes.
2. Hasty; abrupt; done without careful thought.
Joining the Navy so suddenly was a **precipitous** act.

regain
ri gān´

v. To get back.
By following the doctor's orders, I slowly **regained** my health.

slay
slā

v. To kill violently. (**slain**, past participle)
The scene where Saint George **slays** the dragon comes right at the end of the play.

symptom
simp´ təm

n. A sign of something.
Headaches can be a **symptom** of eyestrain.

80

−2

ail
banish
communicate
console
cower
deliberate
depth
desire
livelihood
misfortune
orphan
precipice
regain
slay
symptom

10A Finding Meanings

Choose two phrases to form a sentence that correctly uses a word from Word List 10. Write each sentence in the space provided.

1. (a) To slay someone is to
   (b) To banish someone is to
   (c) send that person away.
   (d) tell that person something.

To banish someone is to send that person away

2. (a) One's misfortune is
   (b) the way one treats other people.
   (c) the way one makes a living.
   (d) One's livelihood is

One's livehood is the way one makes a livin

3. (a) A precipitous drop in price is
   (b) one that is big and unexpected.
   (c) A desirable drop in price is
   (d) one that is very small.

A desirable drop in price is one that is big and unexpected.

4. (a) To communicate something is to   (c) decide not to take it.
   (b) get it back.   (d) To regain something is to

To regain is to get it back.

5. (a) to be loved.   (c) To be ailing is
   (b) to be ill.   (d) To be deliberate is

To be ailing is to be ill.

6. (a) Consolation is   (c) the giving of information.
   (b) Communication is   (d) a series of unlucky events.

Communication is the giving of information.

7. (a) A deliberate change   (c) is one that is agreeable.
   (b) A desirable change   (d) is one that is hardly noticed.

A deliberate change is one that is agreeable.

8. (a) To slay someone is to   (c) To console someone is to
   (b) comfort that person.   (d) fear that person.

To consle someone is to comfort that person.

9. (a) a large sum of money.   (c) the distance from top to bottom.
   (b) Depth is   (d) Misfortune is

Depth is the distance from top to bottom.

10. (a) a close family member.   (c) A symptom is
    (b) a sign of something.   (d) An orphan is

A symptom is a sign of something.

−2

10B Just the Right Word

Improve each of the following sentences by crossing out the bold phrase and replacing it with a word (or a form of the word) from Word List 10.

82

deliberated

1. The judges **gave a great deal of thought and talked among themselves** for a long time before announcing the winner of the science fair.

misfortune

2. The worst **bad luck** to hit the town was the closing of the shipyard.

slay

3. Hunters who **violently kill** baby seals for their fur will be stopped.

4. "You don't look well. What **is the matter with** you?" asked Jorge.

desire

5. He expressed a **strong wish** to spend more time with his children.

precipice

6. It took the climbers an hour to descend the **steep cliff that went straight down**.

cower

7. We used to **shrink back in fear** whenever we heard her voice.

console

8. When Luisa's pet rabbit died, she began writing in her journal every night for **something to give her comfort**.

orphans

9. The **children whose parents had been killed** were all adopted by families in town.

banish

10. If you want this venture to succeed, you must **get rid of** any thoughts of failure.

depths

11. I was moved to the **very deepest parts** of my soul by the sight of the northern lights flashing across the sky.

10C Applying Meanings

Circle the letter of each correct answer to the questions below. A question may have more than one correct answer.

1. Which of the following can have **depth**?
   - (a) a drawer
   - (b) a pond
   - (c) a point
   - (d) a shelf

2. Which of the following might an actor **desire**?
   - (a) perfect teeth
   - (b) applause
   - (c) decayed teeth
   - (d) a good role

3. Which of the following is a way to **communicate**?
   - (a) watching television
   - (b) talking on the phone
   - (c) reading a book
   - (d) writing a letter

4. Which of the following is an **ailment**?
   - (a) measles
   - (b) anger
   - (c) baldness
   - (d) hunger

5. Which of the following might be a person's **livelihood**?
   - (a) attending school
   - (b) mowing lawns
   - (c) washing cars
   - (d) taking out the trash

ail
banish
communicate
console
cower
deliberate
depth
desire
livelihood
misfortune
orphan
precipice
regain
slay
symptom

6. Which of the following might be a **deliberate** act?

   (a) stumbling   (c) lying
   (b) singing   (d) sneezing

7. Which of the following could be **precipitous**?

   (a) a fall in price   (c) a cliff
   (b) an action   (d) a road

8. Which of the following could be **regained**?

   (a) one's youth   (c) the trust of a friend
   (b) one's health   (d) the lead in a race

10D Word Study

Turn to the Word List for this lesson and look up *deliberate*. Notice that it has two different pronunciations. When used as an adjective, the last syllable rhymes with *hut*. When used as a verb, the last syllable rhymes with *late*.

Several other words from earlier lessons are also pronounced differently depending on whether they are used as nouns or verbs. There are two syllables in each word pair below, and we stress (say more forcefully) either the first or the second syllable depending on whether the word is used as a verb or a noun. In the pronunciation guide, an accent mark follows the stressed syllable. The word *banish* is pronounced *ba´ nish*, with the stress falling on the first syllable: BA-nish.

For each sentence below, underline the syllable that is stressed in the word in bold. To the right of each sentence, write whether the word is a verb or a noun.

1. To **project** your voice, you speak to the back of the room. *verb*

2. A **project** of this size will take years to complete. *noun*

3. You can get a parking **permit** at the town hall. *noun*

4. The town does not **permit** overnight parking on Main Street. *verb*

5. We expect to sign the **contract** at tomorrow's meeting. *noun*

6. Metals **contract** as they get colder. *verb*

7. If the pottery is a factory **reject**, we sell it for half price. *noun*

8. If you **reject** your friend's offer, you might regret it later. *verb*

9. We **progress** slowly, one small step at a time. *verb*

10. Tim's latest school report shows he made **progress** in math and science. *noun*

10E Passage

Read the passage below; then complete the exercise that follows.

Tokoyo and the Sea Monster

Folktales are stories passed on from adults to children without ever being written down. Every country has its folktales, and this one comes from Japan. It is the story of a young pearl diver named Tokoyo.

The people of Tokoyo's village made their **livelihood** diving for pearls. Tokoyo was the youngest of the divers. She could stay underwater longer and collect more oysters than anyone, searching for the one oyster in a thousand that contained a precious pearl. The sea was like a second home to her, and she swam easily through its **depths**, cutting oysters from the rocks with her razor-sharp pearling knife.

The other pearl divers were all the family Tokoyo had. Her mother had died when she was a baby, and while she was still a child **misfortune** struck again. Her father, whose sense of humor had gotten him into trouble before, had made a joke about the fact that the emperor was always sick. Because making fun of the emperor was a crime, Tokoyo's father was **banished** to the island of Oki, far from the Japanese mainland. To make matters worse, **communication** between Tokoyo and her father was forbidden. Her friends tried to **console** the young girl, but they could not lift her spirits. She felt like an **orphan**, and the house that had once been filled with laughter was now filled with sorrow.

Tokoyo's one **desire** was to see her father. On her fifteenth birthday, she left her village and set off for Oki. Soon after landing on the island, Tokoyo saw a group of people standing on the edge of a cliff with a girl about her own age who was dressed all in white. People explained to Tokoyo that the evil sea god that made its home in the waters off the island demanded the life of a young girl once a year. They told her that the girl **cowering** before them had been chosen as the sea god's victim and was about to be thrown into the sea. Then they said that the sea god had also cast a spell on the emperor, causing his many **ailments**. When she heard this, Tokoyo saw a chance to help her father. She begged people to let her take the girl's place. They began to **deliberate** among themselves while Tokoyo waited anxiously. Finally, to her great relief, they agreed.

Tokoyo walked to the edge of the **precipice**, took a deep breath, and leaped into the water. She swam deeper and deeper until, at the bottom of the sea, she found herself face to face with the evil sea god. Tokoyo drew her pearling knife, **slaying** the evil sea god and thus ending the spell he had cast on the emperor. In an instant, all the emperor's **symptoms** disappeared. He was delighted to be rid of the doctors who had attended him, and when he learned of Tokoyo's brave deed, he promised the young girl whatever she wanted. As a result of Tokoyo's wish, her father **regained** his freedom and was happily reunited with his daughter.

ail
banish
communicate
console
cower
deliberate
depth
desire
livelihood
misfortune
orphan
precipice
regain
slay
symptom

Answer each of the following questions in the form of a sentence. If a question does not contain a vocabulary word from this lesson's word list, use one in your answer. Use each word only once. Questions and answers will then contain all fifteen words (or forms of the words).

1. Explain why the story of Tokoyo and the evil sea god has a happy ending.

Her father regained his freedom.

2. Was Tokoyo an **orphan**? Explain your answer.

She wasn't because her father was still alive.

3. What does "**misfortune** struck" mean as it is used in the passage?

Something bad happened Tokoyo.

4. Why did the emperor need doctors?

ailing

The emperor needed doctors because he was ailing.

5. How does the narrative make clear that Tokoyo's friends were kind to her?

consoled

Tokoyo's friends consoled her.

6. Where did the evil sea god live?

depths

He lived in the depths of the sea.

7. Explain why Tokoyo's fight with the sea god was a **deliberate** act.

She thought it out carefully.

8. Why didn't Tokoyo's father write to her?

communication

The communication with her father was forbiden.

9. Why was Tokoyo's father living on the island of Oki?

banish

Her father got banished.

10. Why did Tokoyo go to the island of Oki?

desire

Tokoyo's one desire was to see her father.

11. Why had the girl in white been taken to the **precipice**?

Every year the evil sea god demanded a young girls life.

12. How can you tell that the girl in white was afraid?

cowers

The girl cowers to be a victom.

13. Why did Tokoyo want to take the girl's place?

slay

So she can slay the evil sea god.

14. How did the emperor know that the spell had been broken?

sumotom

His symptoms disappeared.

15. Why did the people of Tokoyo's village dive for oysters?

livelihood

That was their livelihood.

FUN & FASCINATING FACTS

One of the world's oldest languages is Sanskrit. It was spoken in India thousands of years ago and is the special language of the Hindu religion. very few people speak it today, but some words in European languages are connected to Sanskrit. **Orphan** is one of them. An *orphan* is a child without parents who therefore can be in a weak and helpless state. The word comes from the Sanskrit *arbha*, which means "weak; helpless."

This lesson includes the word **slay**, which is a homophone of *sleigh*. A *sleigh* is a carriage on runners that travels over snow. *Sleigh* and slay are pronounced the same way.

Lesson 11

Word List

Study the definitions of the words below; then do the exercises for the lesson.

annual
an´ yoo əl

adj. Happening every year.
Somerville's **annual** town meeting is in March.
n. 1. A plant that lives for one year.
Impatiens is my favorite **annual**.
2. A book that comes out once a year.
I save all my NFL football **annuals**.

artificial
är tə fish´ əl

adj. Made by human beings and not by nature.
My Aunt Rosa says she can taste the difference between **artificial** sweeteners and real sugar.

blend
blend

v. 1. To come or mix together into one.
Make sure you **blend** the butter and sugar before you add the flour.
2. To go together.
The painter chose colors that **blend** well.
n. A mixture.
Mocha is a **blend** of chocolate and coffee.

bore
bôr

v. 1. To make a round hole in by drilling.
If you **bore** a hole in the wood first, you won't split it when you put in the screw.
2. To tire by being dull and uninteresting.
The yawns of my listeners told me I was beginning to **bore** them.
n. A dull and uninteresting person.
He tells that same joke so often that he is becoming a terrible **bore**.
boring *adj.* Dull and uninteresting.
She sometimes stretches the facts a little, but her stories are never **boring**.
boredom *n.* A state of being bored.
When heads began to nod and eyes to close, you could tell **boredom** had set in.

considerable
kən sid´ ər ə bəl

adj. Great; large.
Although my grandmother's house is a **considerable** distance from town, she walks to the post office there every day.

crude
krood

adj. 1. Raw; in an unrefined state.
Refineries turn **crude** oil into gasoline.
2. Roughly made.
Andrea drew me a **crude** map with a crayon on a scrap of paper.
3. Ill-mannered.
As we walked back from school, we tried to ignore their **crude** remarks.

evaporate
i va´ pə rāt

v. 1. To change from water into steam or vapor.
The water in the kettle boiled so long that it all **evaporated.**
2. To disappear.
By the third day on the mountain, our hopes of being rescued began to **evaporate**.

foliage fō′ lē ij	*n.* The leaves of trees and other plants. The house at the end of the road was completely hidden by **foliage**.
gash gash	*n.* A long, deep cut. When Liza slipped on the rocks, she had to go to the hospital to have the **gash** in her leg stitched up.
hue hyōo	*n.* A color; especially a shade of color. The poppies in Monet's paintings stand out because of their vivid reddish-orange **hue**.
increase in krēs′	*v.* To make or become larger; to add to. I'm going to ask my mother to **increase** my allowance on my next birthday. *n.* (in′ krēs) The amount by which something gets larger. A wet spring usually means an **increase** in the number of mosquitoes.
nourish nʉr′ ish	*v.* To feed; to support or make grow. We **nourish** our bodies best by eating a diet of fruits, vegetables, and grains. **nourishment** *n.* Anything that feeds or helps to make grow. When I had the flu, the only **nourishment** I could take was clear chicken broth.
vary ver′ ē	*v.* To make or have a change in. The length of a calendar month **varies** between twenty-eight and thirty-one days. **variation** (ver ē ā′ shən) *n.* A change in form, position, or condition. There isn't much **variation** between the summer and the winter temperatures where my grandfather lives.
vision vi′ zhən	*n.* 1. Eyesight. If you are lucky enough to have 20/20 **vision**, you'll be able to see well. 2. Something seen in the mind, especially of the future. The founders of the United Nations had a **vision** of a world without hunger or war. **visual** *adj.* Of or used in seeing. As a **visual** aid, the speaker projected pictures onto a large screen.
yield yēld	*v.* 1. To give up someone or something; to surrender. Congress finally **yielded** to the president's demands and passed the budget. 2. To produce. Twenty gallons of milk will **yield** about one pound of butter. *n.* The amount produced. The farmer told us that you can expect a **yield** of about fifty pounds of fruit from each apple tree.

11A Finding Meanings

Choose two phrases to form a sentence that correctly uses a word from Word List 11. Write each sentence in the space provided.

1. (a) one that is quite large.
   (b) A considerable amount is
   (c) An increased amount is
   (d) one that is reduced.

A considerable amount is one that is quite large.

2. (a) is not fully developed.
   (b) An artificial aid is one that
   (c) A visual aid is one that
   (d) helps one to see.

A visual aid is one that helps one see.

3. (a) A blend is
   (b) a long, deep cut.
   (c) A bore is
   (d) a dull and uninteresting person.

A bore is a dull and unintresting person

4. (a) A gash is
   (b) a round hole made by a drill.
   (c) something that appears once a year.
   (d) An annual is

An anual is something that apears once a year

5. (a) To increase is
   (b) to be mixed together.
   (c) to grow.
   (d) To evaporate is

To increase is to grow.

6. (a) Crude rubber is
   (b) Artificial rubber is
   (c) still in a raw state.
   (d) a mixture of different kinds.

Crude rubber is still in raw state.

7. (a) Colors that blend are those that
   (b) go well together.
   (c) quickly fade.
   (d) Colors that vary are those that

Colors that blend are those that go well together

8. (a) A gash is
   (b) a deep cut.
   (c) a careless remark.
   (d) A hue is

A gash is a deep cut.

9. (a) to give way.
   (b) To yield is
   (c) To evaporate is
   (d) to melt.

To yield is to give away.

10. (a) the wood that comes from it.
    (b) A tree's foliage is
    (c) its leaves.
    (d) A tree's hue is

A tree's foliage is its leaves.

11. (a) Something that nourishes
    (b) Something that varies
    (c) does not stay the same.
    (d) keeps getting smaller.

Something that varies does not stay the same.

11B Just the Right Word

Improve each of the following sentences by crossing out the bold phrase and replacing it with a word (or a form of the word) from Word List 11. −2

80

1. The *considerable* ~~amount produced~~ from these oil wells is a thousand barrels a day.

2. Basil is a(n) *annual* ~~plant that grows for just one season~~.

3. Mr. Martinez loves to talk about his new computer, but he can get very *boring* ~~dull and uninteresting~~.

4. Spilled gasoline *evaporates* ~~turns to vapor~~ and mixes with the air quickly.

5. Manure *nourish* ~~provides food for~~ growing plants.

6. The *crude* ~~roughly made~~ drawing was the work of a very young child.

7. Julio's favorite sandwich filling is made by *blending* ~~mixing together~~ peanut butter and honey.

8. These interior paints come in many different *hues* ~~shades of color~~.

9. Isabel is a person whose *vision* ~~sense of the future~~ of the city's parks will be appealing to both young and old.

10. The flowers on the piano look so real that you cannot tell they are *artificial* ~~made by human hands~~.

63

11C Applying Meanings

−3

Circle the letter of each correct answer to the questions below. A question may have more than one correct answer.

1. Which of the following might **evaporate**?
   (a) coal
   (b) water
   (c) gasoline
   (d) electricity

2. Which of the following is an **increase**?
   (a) from Maine to Mexico
   (b) from A to Z
   (c) from a scarcity to a surplus
   (d) from several to many

3. Which of the following is a **considerable** amount?
   (a) ten cents
   (b) a thousand dollars
   (c) fifty tons
   (d) a modest sum

annual
artificial
blend
bore
considerable
crude
evaporate
foliage
gash
hue
increase
nourish
vary
vision
yield

4. Which of the following have **foliage**?

(a) rose bushes   (c) cactus plants

(b) apple trees   (d) garden vegetables

5. Which of the following could cause a **gash**?

(a) a sharp rock   (c) a hammer

(b) a baseball   (d) an ax

6. Which of the following is a **hue**?

(a) pink   (c) clear

(b) yellow   (d) dark

7. For which of the following would you need your **vision**?

(a) making sure your socks match   (c) listening to the radio

(b) observing Thanksgiving   (d) observing the moon

8. Which of the following would a seven-year-old probably find **boring**?

(a) a visit to a circus   (c) a speech by a state senator

(b) a ride on a roller coaster   (d) a TV discussion of proper diet

11D Word Study

Write the antonym of each word on the left on the line next to it. Choose from the words on the right, which are in a different order.

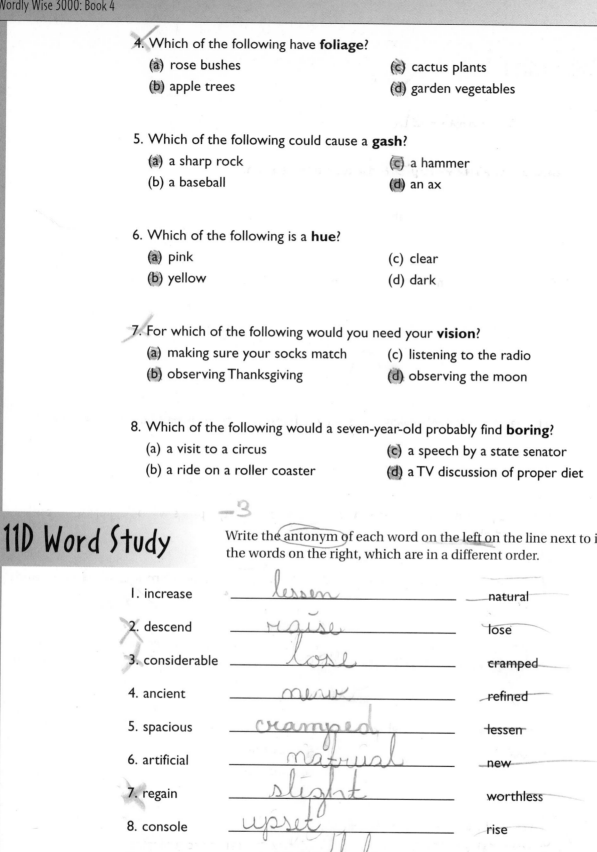

1. increase   _lessen_   natural

2. descend   _raise_   lose

3. considerable _lose_   cramped

4. ancient   _new_   refined

5. spacious   _cramped_   lessen

6. artificial   _natural_   new

7. regain   _slight_   worthless

8. console   _upset_   rise

9. precious   _worthless_   slight

10. crude   _refined_   upset

11E Passage

Read the passage below; then complete the exercise that follows.

Maple Sugaring

In the late fall, one of nature's most magnificent sights is the **foliage** of New England's maple trees, blazing with color. The many **hues** range from the fiery reds of the swamp maples to the rich golds of the sugar maples.

In the spring, though, some trees offer more than just a **visual** treat. Early in the season, buckets dangle from the sides of sugar maples, collecting sap for the **annual** maple sugaring.

The amount of sap that can be collected from a healthy tree **varies** between twelve and twenty gallons, which will **yield** from two to four pounds of maple syrup. This will leave plenty of sap for the tree to **nourish** itself as it enters a new growing season.

The weather has a great deal to do with how much sap a tree produces. The flow is greatest when the days are sunny and the nights are cold. The flow of sap slows down at night and **increases** during the day. Maple trees in low, wet areas produce more sap than trees growing in higher and drier parts, but the sap contains less sugar.

Native Americans showed the first settlers how to make maple syrup. They used to make **gashes** in the trees with axes in order to let the sap run out, but this could cause **considerable** damage to the tree. Today, tree farmers **bore** a small hole into each tree, about three feet above the ground, and this does no harm.

When it trickles from the tree, the syrup is in **crude** form; it needs to be refined before it is ready to use. It is boiled in large kettles until the water **evaporates**. The syrup that remains is passed through filters to clean it. It is then ready to be poured on waffles and pancakes or made into the maple sugar candy so popular with visitors to New England.

Maple syrup is produced only in North America in a season that lasts four to six weeks. Besides New England, maple sugaring is carried out in several other northern states, as well as the Canadian provinces of Quebec and Ontario. Much of the syrup that Americans pour on their pancakes is not real maple syrup, however. It is made from cane sugar syrup with **artificial** maple flavoring added. The makers may **blend** it with real maple syrup so that the label can say "Contains Real Maple Syrup." One hundred percent maple syrup costs more, but those who enjoy its taste say that there is nothing like the real thing.

annual
artificial
blend
bore
considerable
crude
evaporate
foliage
gash
hue
increase
nourish
vary
vision
yield

Answer each of the following questions in the <u>form of a sentence.</u> If a question does not contain a vocabulary word from this lesson's word list, <u>use one in your answer.</u> Use each word only once. Questions and answers will then contain all fifteen words (or forms of the words).

1. What do the words "Contains Real Maple Syrup" on the label tell you?

The makers may blend it with real syrup.

2. Why do you think **artificial** maple syrup costs less than the real thing?

The artificial maple syrup cost less because it is not real.

3. What is another word for the leaves of a tree?

Foliage is another word for leaves.

4. In what season do maple trees become a **visual** treat?

It becomes a visual treat in the spring.

5. If you were hiking in New England in the fall, what **hues** might you see?

You will see fiery reds of the swamp maples to rich gold.

varies

6. How much sap can be collected from a sugar maple?

A healthy tree varies between twelve and twenty gallons.

7. What is the meaning of **yield** as it is used in the passage?

In the passage it means to stop.

nourish

8. Why do trees produce sap?

The tree nourish itself as it enters a new season.

increases

9. Why do you think people gathering sap prefer sunny days?

Sap increases during the day

gashes

10. Why did the first settlers need axes to get at the sap?

They had to make gashes so the sap could come out.

considerable

11. Why don't people use this method any more?

It causes considerable amount of damage to trees.

bore

12. Explain why you might see small round holes in the trunks of sugar maples.

Tree farmers bore a small into each tree about three feet above the ground.

crude

13. Why don't people use the syrup that collects in the buckets immediately?

When it trickles from the tree, the syrup is in crude form.

14. What happens when sap is boiled?

evaporates

15. How often does maple sugaring occur?

annual

Maple suguring acures annually

FUN & FASCINATING FACTS

Here are two more pairs of homophones. The first is **bore** and *boar*; a *boar* is a male pig. The second is **hue** and *hew*; to *hew* something is to cut it or chop it with an ax.

Crude and *refined* are antonyms. (*Crude* sugar is purified by boiling and filtering; it then becomes *refined* sugar.)

Another word for steam is *vapor*. It comes unchanged from the Latin word *vapor*, which means "steam." The Latin prefix *ex-* means "out;" before certain letters, *ex-* is shortened to *e-*. This happens with the word **evaporate**. When water *e-vapor-ates* by being warmed, the water in the form of steam, or *vapor*, is drawn *out* into the air.

Lesson 12

> **Word List** Study the definitions of the words below; then do the exercises for the lesson.

ability
ə bi´ lə te

n. Power or knowledge; skill.
Lani's **ability** to do math problems in her head astounded her teacher.

amiable
ā´ mē ə bəl

adj. Friendly; good natured and pleasant.
My uncle's **amiable** manner put my friends at ease right away.

bliss
blis

n. Complete joy or happiness.
My idea of **bliss** is an afternoon on the river with my fishing rod.
blissful *adj.* Very happy; joyful.
The proud parents wore **blissful** smiles as they watched their son graduate.

caress
kə res´

v. To touch in a tender or loving way.
Sean **caressed** the baby's forehead gently as it lay sleeping.
n. A tender or loving touch or hug.
The kitten brushing against my cheek felt like a **caress**.

clutch
kluch

v. To grasp or hold tightly to.
Kabir **clutched** his teddy bear as he climbed into the dentist's chair.
n. The part of a machine that connects and disconnects the power from the rest of the machine.
Before changing gears in a standard shift car, first step on the **clutch**.

coax
kōks

v. To persuade or urge in a gentle way.
I **coaxed** my baby sister into holding my hand as we crossed the street.

furious
fyoor´ ē əs

adj. 1. Very, very angry.
The emperor was **furious** when he realized how the two "tailors" had tricked him.
2. Very fast, strong, or wild.
I was confused by the **furious** activity going on in the kitchen.
fury *n.* 1. Great anger.
Mark's uneasiness turned to **fury** when he learned how completely he had been tricked.
2. Wild and uncontrolled force.
The **fury** of the storm was far greater than had been forecast.

gesture
jes´ chər

n. 1. A movement of the arm or hand.
The president waved his arm in a farewell **gesture** before boarding Air Force One.
2. Something done to show one's feelings.
Asking you to the birthday party was Dolores's **gesture** of friendship.
v. To make a movement of the arm or hand.
The coach **gestured** to the players on the bench to join her on the field.

mope
mōp

v. To be sad and gloomy; to lose interest in the things that usually bring pleasure.
As the long, hot summer days went on and I still had no job, I began to **mope**.

prefer
pri fər´

v. To like better; to choose first.
Which do you **prefer**, chocolate or vanilla?
preference (pre´ fər əns) *n.* That which is preferred.
If you don't have a **preference**, I'll choose the movie.

recover
ri kuv´ ər

v. 1. To get back to a normal state; to get well again.
Patrizia soon **recovered** from the flu.
2. To get back what was lost or stolen.
It cost a hundred dollars to **recover** my car after it was towed.
recovery *n.* 1. A return to a normal state.
Dr. Holberg was surprised at the speed of my **recovery**.
2. The act of getting back what was lost or stolen.
The museum is offering a reward for the **recovery** of the missing painting.

replace
ri plās´

v. 1. To take the place of.
Who will **replace** Mr. Myers when he leaves the school?
2. To put back in place.
When you are through with the encyclopedias, let the librarian **replace** them on the shelves.
replacement *n.* A person or thing that takes the place of another.
If the water pump cannot be repaired, the plumber will order a **replacement** for us.

request
ri kwest´

v. To ask for.
I **requested** a chocolate cake with cherry frosting for my birthday.
n. The thing asked for.
The band leader agreed to play our **request**.

separate
se´ pər āt

v. To set or keep apart.
Whenever the twins start fighting, my mother **separates** them.
adj. (se´ pər ət) Not together; not joined.
The twins asked if they could have **separate** bedrooms.

shun
shun

v. To take special pains to avoid; to keep away from.
Leon ceased his bullying when his classmates started to **shun** him.

12A Finding Meanings

Choose two phrases to form a sentence that correctly uses a word from Word List 12. Write each sentence in the space provided.

1. (a) To shun something
   (b) To recover something
   (c) is to want it very badly.
   (d) is to have nothing to do with it.

To shun something is to have nothing to do with it

2. (a) To be amiable is to be
   (b) very angry.
   (c) talkative.
   (d) To be furious is to be

To be furious is to be very angry.

3. (a) To separate people is to   (c) try to persuade them to do something.
    (b) make them angry.   (d) To coax people is to

To coax people is to try to persuade them to do something

4. (a) To prefer something is   (c) To recover something is
    (b) to get it back.   (d) to get closer to it.

To recover something is to get it back.

5. (a) A caress is   (c) a warm and loving touch.
    (b) A request is   (d) a warning of possible danger.

A caress is a warm and loving touch.

6. (a) To clutch something is to   (c) To prefer something is to
    (b) like it better than something else.   (d) let go of it.

To prefer something is to like it better than something else.

7. (a) To separate something is to   (c) To request something is to
    (b) ask for it.   (d) hold tightly to it.

To request something is to ask for it.

8. (a) A gesture is   (c) someone who takes the place of another.
    (b) A replacement is   (d) something said as a joke.

A replacement is someone who takes the place of another.

9. (a) great anger.   (c) Bliss is
    (b) deep sadness.   (d) Fury is

Fury is great anger.

10. (a) A clutch is   (c) a warning not to get any closer.
    (b) A gesture is   (d) a movement of the arm or hand.

A gesture is a movement of the arm or hand.

12B Just the Right Word

Improve each of the following sentences by crossing out the bold phrase and replacing it with a word (or a form of the word) from Word List 12.

−2

80

1. Andrea and Lucia have to be **kept apart** *separated* because they giggle so much if they sit together.

2. I **made a movement of my arm** *gestured* to draw attention to the car I was interested in driving.

3. I had just one **thing I wanted to ask for,** *request* and that was a large glass of cold lemonade.

4. Irina had the chicken pox, but made a quick **return to good health**. *recover*

5. Angela **lost interest in the things that usually gave her pleasure** for weeks after Julio moved away. *moped*

6. Our old car needs a new **part that connects and disconnects power from the engine**. *clutch*

7. Around 1900, the automobile began to **take the place of** the horse and buggy. *replace*

8. My **having knowledge of how** to speak Spanish was what got me the job in the office. *ability*

9. The runners set off at a **very fast** pace. *furious*

10. A look of **complete happiness** crossed Mai-ying's face when she heard that she had won the scholarship. *bliss*

12C Applying Meanings

Circle the letter of each correct answer to the questions below. A question may have more than one correct answer.

1. Which of the following would an **amiable** person do?
   (a) avoid other people
   (b) greet you with a smile
   (c) get angry easily
   (d) make friends easily

2. Which of the following might a child **caress**?
   (a) a baby sister
   (b) a stuffed animal
   (c) a pet rabbit
   (d) a porcupine

3. Which of the following might a person **clutch**?
   (a) a phone call
   (b) a telephone
   (c) a baseball bat
   (d) a baseball score

4. Which of the following is a friendly **gesture**?
   (a) sending a get-well card
   (b) closing your eyes
   (c) holding out your hand
   (d) turning your back

5. Which of the following might a person who is **moping** do?
   (a) suggest having a party
   (b) not answer when spoken to
   (c) stay home all day
   (d) call up old friends

ability
amiable
bliss
caress
clutch
coax
furious
gesture
mope
prefer
recover
replace
request
separate
shun

6. Which of the following could be **recovered**?
   - (a) lost time
   - (b) a lost ring
   - (c) your balance
   - (d) your health

7. Which of the following can be **replaced**?
   - (a) a book taken from the shelf
   - (b) a lost screwdriver
   - (c) a friend who dies
   - (d) a pet turtle that dies

8. Who would someone be likely to **shun**?
   - (a) an enemy
   - (b) an untrustworthy person
   - (c) a friend
   - (d) a helpful person

12D Word Study

Synonyms are words with similar meanings, but the meanings are not always exactly the same. Read the pairs of sentences below. Then choose the synonym that best fits each sentence.

ask/request

1. When I am lost, I usually _ask_ someone for directions.

2. The driver will let you get out of the bus at Hanover Street only if you _request_ a stop there.

shun/avoid

3. I try to _avoid_ the downtown area at rush hour.

4. The students _shun_ anyone who acts like a bully.

slay/kill

5. In the legend, the hero set out to _slay_ the dragon.

6. In the movie, we saw a lion _kill_ a zebra after bringing it down.

desire/wish

7. Did your _wish_ come true?

8. Their one _desire_ was to live in freedom.

bliss/happiness

9. _Happiness_ can often be found by serving others.

10. To be young and in love was sheer _bliss_ .

old/ancient

11. The _ancient_ city of Nineveh was in present-day Iraq.

12. Do you have any _old_ clothes you want to give away?

alter/change

13. Do you intend to _alter_ the date of the meeting?

14. A tailor can _change_ that jacket so that it fits better.

12E Passage

Read the passage below; then complete the exercise that follows.

Communicating with Koko

American Sign Language (ASL) is a form of communication that is as rich and flexible as spoken English. It is used by hundreds of thousands of hearing-impaired people. Each **gesture** of the hand or arm has a particular meaning. In the early 1970s, a most unusual student began learning to communicate through ASL. Her name was Koko and her teacher was Dr. Francine Patterson.

Koko, a gorilla, was born in the San Francisco Zoo. While still a baby, she became ill and had to be **separated** from the other gorillas. She lived in a specially equipped trailer, where Dr. Patterson, a scientist interested in animal behavior, took care of her. While Dr. Patterson was nursing Koko back to health, she slowly and with great difficulty taught the young gorilla to communicate, using ASL hand and arm movements.

Dr. Patterson made up little games to teach Koko how to use her hands. She began by working on words for food and drink, showing her the object, saying the word, and making the sign. For example, she would sign the word for drink before giving Koko a drink. Koko began to show signs that she understood the meaning of Dr. Patterson's gestures after only two weeks. Once she made the association between hand movements and the objects they represented, she quickly began to learn words. By eighteen months, she knew twenty-two signs; by three years and three months, she could make seventy-eight understandable signs. Over a period of six years, she learned over a thousand words and could even string words together to form simple sentences.

Dr. Patterson also used picture books to teach Koko new words. Koko **preferred** looking at books with pictures of gorillas and cats, so when Dr. Patterson asked Koko what she wanted for her birthday, she wasn't surprised when Koko **requested** a cat. Koko was usually a very **amiable** creature, but when she opened Dr. Patterson's present and saw a stuffed animal, she was **furious** and threw it away. Dr. Patterson tried to **coax** the unhappy gorilla to play with the toy cat, but her attempts failed. Koko knew the difference between a real cat and a toy one, and she **shunned** the stuffed animal completely. She wanted a real cat.

A few weeks later Dr. Patterson gave Koko a little gray kitten. Koko picked up the kitten very carefully and **caressed** it gently. When asked what she was going to call it, she signed "All Ball." Perhaps she gave it this name because it had no tail, and without a tail it looked just like a ball of fur. As Koko carried All Ball around on her back, the kitten **clutched** Koko's fur, the way baby gorillas do with their mothers. Koko loved to play games with All Ball; the two became close friends.

ability
amiable
bliss
caress
clutch
coax
furious
gesture
mope
prefer
recover
replace
request
separate
shun

One day All Ball was hit by a car and died. For days afterward, Koko **moped**—miserable over the loss of her friend. Koko **recovered** her good spirits when Dr. Patterson gave her another kitten to **replace** All Ball. When Koko got her new pet, she picked it up and held it lovingly, a **blissful** look on her face.

With language comes the **ability** to make jokes—and also to lie. Koko learned to do both. One day she broke the sink in the trailer. When Dr. Patterson asked her who had done it, Koko signed the name of the person who had been in the trailer with her. Another time she pointed to a white towel and signed "red." She was corrected several times but refused to admit she had made a mistake. Then she slyly picked a tiny piece of lint off the towel. It was red!

Answer each of the following questions in the form of a sentence. If a question does not contain a vocabulary word from this lesson's word list, use one in your answer. Use each word only once. Questions and answers will then contain all fifteen words (or forms of the words).

1. What is the meaning of **gesture** as it is used in the passage?

A type of movement of the hand or arm.

2. Why was Koko living in a trailer?

Koko got seperated from the other gorillas because of her illness

3. Did Koko show a **preference** for a particular kind of book?

She preferred a book with cats and gorillas.

4. Why did Dr. Patterson choose a cat to give Koko?

Koko requested that she wanted a cat.

5. What kind of personality did Koko have?

Koko was usually a very amiable creature.

6. What is the meaning of **furious** as it is used in the passage?

It means that she was really mad.

7. How did Koko respond to Dr. Patterson's coaxing?

Dr. Patterson bought her a cat.

8. Why did Koko **shun** the toy cat?

She wanted a real cat.

9. How did Koko show that she cherished the real kitten?

caressed

Koko picked up the kitten and caressed it gentl

10. How did All Ball stay on Koko's back?

clutch

All Ball clutched on her back

11. How could Dr. Patterson tell that Koko was sad when All Ball died?

moped

Koko moped for days.

12. What is the meaning of **replace** as it is used in the passage?

It means to take place of something.

13. How could Dr. Patterson tell that Koko was happy with the second cat?

recovered

Koko recovered her good spirits.

14. What did learning to communicate allow Koko to do?

ability

With language comes the ability to make jokes and lie.

15. How would you feel if you felt **blissful**?

If I was blissful I would feel very happy.

FUN & FASCINATING FACTS

You are likely to **caress** those who are most dear to you. This is not surprising, since the word comes from the Latin *caro*, which means "dear." You might think that the word *care* comes from this same Latin root since we care for those who are dear to us, but it comes from something totally different: the Old English word *cearu*.

The noun **clutch** has an unusual meaning when it is used as the plural noun *clutches*. To be "in the clutches" of something or somebody is to be in the power of that thing or that person. People who are taken hostage are in the *clutches* of those who have taken them prisoner; criminals spend a lot of time trying to avoid the *clutches* of the law.

Review for Lessons 9–12

Hidden Message In the boxes provided, write the words from Lessons 9 through 12 that are missing in each of the sentences below. The number following each sentence gives the word list from which the missing word is taken. When the exercise is finished, the shaded boxes should spell out an interesting observation from the English writer, philospher, and mathematician Bertrand Russell.

1. Marathon runners cover a _____ of over twenty-six miles. (9)

2. The _____ in my leg is healing quickly. (11)

3. New York was once a small _____ at the tip of Manhattan. (9)

4. Rebecca was in _____ until her lost kitten was found. (9)

5. The _____ means of escape was through an underground tunnel. (9)

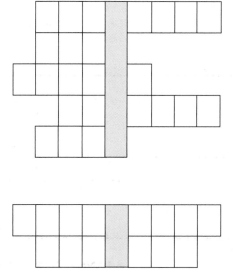

6. I stood on the edge of the _____ and looked down. (10)

7. We tried to _____ him for the loss of his pet rabbit. (10)

8. This year's _____ meeting will be held in May. (11)

9. After a year's hard work, I was able to _____ my place on the team. (10)

10. When food is _____ , people can go hungry. (9)

11. Buy low and sell high is a _____ way of doing business. (9)

12. Being light on her feet is a(n) _____ for a ballerina. (9)

13. The magician promised us that her next trick would _____ us. (9)

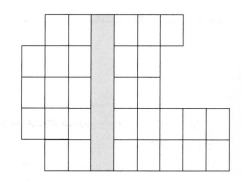

14. We built a _____ shelter from cardboard boxes. (11)

15. My wages will _____ from $200 to $250 a week. (11)

16. Their calm manner helped _____ our fears. (10)

17. My brother has the _____ to become an excellent singer. (12)

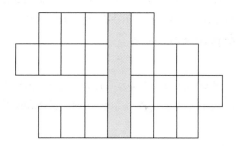

18. The sun's warmth causes the water to _____ . (11)

19. The Senate will _____ the new Secretary of Education. (9)

20. A headache could be a _____ of flu. (10)

21. My _____ came from buying and selling cars. (10)

22. The breeze was gentle as a _____ on their faces. (12)

23. We tried to _____ them into staying a little longer. (12)

24. David was able to _____ Goliath with a slingshot. (10)

25. We hope to make the family gathering a(n) _____ event. (11)

26. We stayed in _____ rooms at the hotel. (12)

27. Annie Lennox gets thousands of _____ for her autograph. (12)

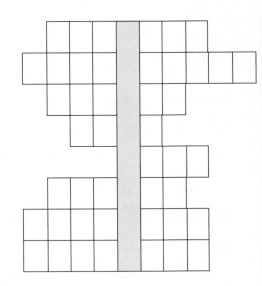

28. The _____ of the water is about ten feet. (10)

29. I had the _____ to lose my suitcase when I changed trains. (10)

30. Andros and Helen made a _____ effort to help the new students. (10)

31. The cause of my _____ puzzled the doctors. (10)

32. The trees lose their _____ in the fall. (11)

33. The host's _____ manner put us at ease. (12)

34. My dad was _____ with me for lying to him. (12)

35. Romulus and Remus were said to be the _____ of Rome. (9)

36. The rose was of a pale yellow _____ . (11)

37. This is a _____ of Brazilian and Kenyan coffees. (11)

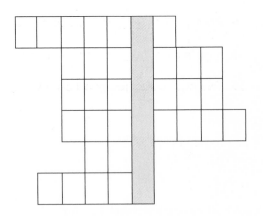

38. I prefer real flowers to _____ ones. (11)

39. What you earn at the print shop will _____ from week to week. (11)

40. The doctor said my uncle would _____ very quickly. (12)

41. When I have nothing to read on vacations, I sometimes _____ . (12)

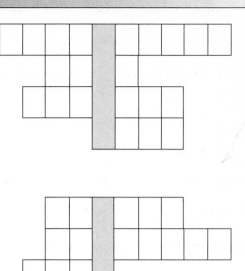

42. I felt the person next to me _____ my arm. (12)

43. The police officer _____ to us to cross the street. (12)

44. It would _____ me to listen to the same story again. (11)

45. It was _____ to lie on the beach without a care. (12)

46. Do you _____ spinach or broccoli? (12)

47. A _____ of old classmates showed up for the school reunion. (9)

48. _____ fatty foods if you want to stay healthy. (12)

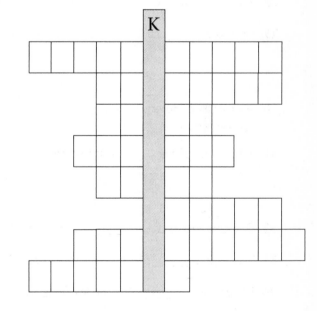

49. We usually _____ by letter. (10)

50. The weather forecast gave little _____ of rain. (9)

51. Why does the dog _____ when you approach it? (10)

52. You need to _____ the damaged parts. (12)

53. This field should _____ two tons of potatoes. (11)

54. My greatest _____ was to complete college. (10)

55. Raja had no _____ that something might go wrong. (9)

56. The cool water felt good on my _____ throat. (9)

Lesson 13

Word List Study the definitions of the words below; then do the exercises for the lesson.

appall
ə pôl´

v. To cause horror, shock, or dismay.
The inspectors were **appalled** by the conditions in the prison factories.
appalling   *adj.* Causing shock and horror.
The television report exposed the **appalling** treatment of the farm workers.

dejected
di jək´ təd

adj. Discouraged; low in spirits.
Jesse felt **dejected** when he couldn't find an apartment with low rent.

depend
di pend´

v. 1. To rely on for support.
Many blind persons **depend** on guide dogs.
2. To be based on.
Whether or not I go to the concert **depends** on what my parents say.
dependable   *adj.* Reliable.
If you do a lot of driving, you need a **dependable** car.

dreary
drir´ ē

adj. Sad and gloomy.
I pulled up the shades to let more light into Olga's dark and **dreary** apartment.

fanatic
fə nat´ ik

n. A person whose enthusiasm for a belief is extreme.
Uncle Roger ran the restaurant for years, and he was a **fanatic** about cleanliness in the kitchen.
fanatical   *adj.* Carrying an interest or enthusiasm to extremes.
Mr. Gradgrind was a **fanatical** believer in the importance of facts.

impact
im´ pakt

n. 1. The striking of one object by another.
The **impact** of the ball bruised the catcher's arm.
2. Forceful impression.
Martin Luther King, Jr.'s "I Have a Dream" speech had a great **impact** on millions of Americans.

invade
in vād´

v. 1. To enter by force in order to take over.
The German army **invaded** Russia in June, 1941.
2. To intrude; to enter in great numbers.
I am putting a lock on my drawer so my little sister won't be able to **invade** my privacy any more.
invasion   *n.* The act of invading.
The gypsy moth **invasion** caused the destruction of many Cape Cod pine trees.

isolate
ī´ sə lāt

v. To cut off from others.
As soon as my brother broke out in spots the doctor **isolated** him for a week.
isolation (ī sə lā´ shən) *n.* The condition of being isolated.
The cottage's **isolation** makes it appealing to someone seeking a quiet vacation.
isolated   *adj.* Cut off from others.
The lighthouse keeper actually enjoyed her **isolated** life.

occupy
ä´ kyoo pī

v. I. To live in; to take up.
My Aunt Bianca's family **occupied** the apartment next to us when I was little.
2. To take over by force.
Protesting students **occupied** the school president's office.
occupation (ä´ kyoo pā´ shən) *n.* I. A person's job or profession.
Nursing is a perfect **occupation** for my brother since he loves helping people.
2. A filling up of time or space.
The sign in the elevator said that **occupation** by more than twelve people was against the law.

reveal
ri vēl´

v. I. To make known.
If you **reveal** the wish you made, it might not come true.
2. To bring into view; to show.
The curtain rose to **reveal** three men sitting on top of a stone wall.

rout
rout

n. A disorganized retreat from an attack; a total defeat.
The battle ended in a **rout** as the enemy soldiers dropped their weapons and ran.
v. To defeat completely.
The U.S. basketball players **routed** their opponents in the 1992 Olympic Games.

suspect
sə spekt´

v. I. To think of as probably guilty.
The police **suspect** the man who used to live upstairs of breaking in to our apartment.
2. To suppose that something is true.
I **suspect** that she knows more algebra than she thinks she does.
n. (sus´ pekt) A person believed to be guilty.
The **suspect** asked to see a lawyer before being questioned.

temporary
tem´ pə rer e

adj. Lasting or made to last for a short time.
The town hall provided a **temporary** place for people to stay during the hurricane.

terror
ter´ ər

n. Great fear.
Thunder and lightening always fill my grandmother with **terror**.
terrify *v.* To fill with terror or great fear.
The reports of the crime in the neighborhood **terrified** the residents.

tragic
tra´ jik

adj. Causing great sadness; terrible or dreadful.
The entire nation grieved over the **tragic** death of Dr. Martin Luther King, Jr.
tragedy (tra´ jə dē) *n.* I. An event that causes great pain, suffering, or loss of life.
The closing of the shipyard would be a **tragedy** for Charlestown.
2. A play that ends sadly as the hero or heroine loses at the end of a great struggle.
Shakespeare wrote some of the world's greatest **tragedies**.

13A Finding Meanings

Choose two phrases to form a sentence that correctly uses a word from Word List 13. Write each sentence in the space provided.

1. (a) travel through it.
   (b) live in it.
   (c) To isolate a place is to
   (d) To occupy a place is to

To occupy is to live in it.

2. (a) A dependable person
   (b) A dejected person
   (c) takes things in stride.
   (d) is in low spirits.

A dejected person is in low spirits.

3. (a) Impact is
   (b) a forceful impression.
   (c) a desire to do good.
   (d) Terror is

Impact is a forceful impression.

4. (a) rely on that person.
   (b) To appall someone is to
   (c) play a joke on that person.
   (d) To depend on someone is to

To depend on someone is to rely on that person.

5. (a) To reveal a place is to
   (b) To invade a place is to
   (c) make changes in it.
   (d) enter it to take over.

To invade a place is to enter it to take over.

6. (a) well cared for.
   (b) To be fanatic is to be
   (c) cut off from others.
   (d) To be isolated is to be

To be isolated is to be cut off from others.

7. (a) To suspect something is to
   (b) bring it into view.
   (c) be afraid of it.
   (d) To reveal something is to

To reveal something is to bring it into view.

8. (a) A dreary event is one
   (b) that causes great sadness.
   (c) that lasts a short time.
   (d) A tragic event is one

A tragic event is one that causes great sadness.

9. (a) To suspect someone is to
   (b) believe that person to be guilty.
   (c) make fun of that person.
   (d) To appall someone is to

To suspect someone is to believe that person be guilty.

10. (a) A rout is
    (b) one who has extreme beliefs.
    (c) a path that is traveled.
    (d) A fanatic is

A fanatic is one who has extreme beliefs.

appall
dejected
depend
dreary
fanatic
impact
invade
isolate
occupy
reveal
rout
suspect
temporary
terror
tragic

13B Just the Right Word

Improve each of the following sentences by crossing out the bold phrase and replacing it with a word (or a form of the word) from Word List 13.

1. Whether or not I go on the trip to the mountains will **be based** on the condition of my car. *depend*

2. The school building seems **dull and gloomy** during winter vacation. *dreary*

3. A person with measles should be **kept away from other people**. *isolate*

4. My job making pizza is **not expected to last for very long**, but I love it. *temporary*

5. I was **shocked and dismayed** to find out that my neighbors had had no heat in their house for four days. *apalled*

6. When cockroaches **moved in and took over** our kitchen, my mother called the landlord immediately. *invaded*

7. The detective waited to question the **persons believed to be guilty of the crime** until their lawyer arrived. *suspect*

8. There was a look of **great fear** in her eyes as she heard the crash of thunder. *terror*

9. The Red Sox **completely defeated** the Yankees by a score of 10 to 0. *routed*

10. *Hamlet* is one of Shakespeare's most famous **plays that end sadly as the hero loses at the end of a great struggle**. *tragedies*

13C Applying Meanings

Circle the letter of each correct answer to the questions below. A question may have more than one correct answer.

1. Which of the following should you be able to **depend** on?
   (a) a close friend
   (b) your parents
   (c) a stranger
   (d) a scoundrel

2. Which of the following could you **reveal**?
   (a) your age
   (b) your date of birth
   (c) your weight
   (d) your plans for the future

3. Which final basketball score(s) would be a **rout**?

    (a) 102 to 98   (c) 110 to 108

    (b) 68 to 12   (d) 72 to 10

4. Which of the following might be thought **dreary**?

    (a) a blissful afternoon   (c) an afternoon spent pulling up weeds

    (b) a bright hue   (d) a person who lacks a sense of humor

5. Which of the following could be **temporary**?

    (a) a death   (c) a shelter

    (b) a job   (d) a period without rain

6. Which of the following would have an **impact**?

    (a) the death of a president   (c) the loss of one's job

    (b) a leaf landing on the ground   (d) a car hitting a tree

7. Which of the following might be **appalling**?

    (a) an increase in crime   (c) the condition of homeless people

    (b) world hunger   (d) the number of people in prison

8. Which of the following is an **occupation**?

    (a) poet   (c) uncle

    (b) lawyer   (d) teacher

appall
dejected
depend
dreary
fanatic
impact
invade
isolate
occupy
reveal
rout
suspect
temporary
terror
tragic

13D Word Study

Here are nine Latin roots and their meanings. Many English words are based on these roots.

tempus	(time)	*amicus*	(friend)
jacere	(to throw)	*rumpere*	(to break)
annus	(year)	*centum*	(hundred)
visus	(to see)	*locus*	(place)
solus	(alone)		

Fill in the blank spaces in each sentence below with the correct Latin root and its meaning. Choose from the list of Latin roots.

1. To **isolate** someone is to cut that person off from others. The word comes from the Latin _solus_, meaning _alone_.

2. An **abrupt** change is one that breaks with the past and comes without warning. The word comes from the Latin _rumpere_, meaning _to break_.

3. To see properly, you need good **vision**. The word comes from the Latin ___*visus*___, meaning _to see_.

4. A **century** is a period of one hundred years. The word comes from the Latin ___*centum*___, meaning _hundred_.

5. A **temporary** position is not expected to last a long time. The word comes from the Latin ___*tempus*___, meaning _time_.

6. To **revise** something is to look it over and make necessary changes. The word comes from the Latin ___*visus*___, meaning _to see_.

7. An **amiable** manner is one that is friendly. The word comes from the Latin ___*amicus*___, meaning _friend_.

8. An **annual** event is one that is held every year. The word comes from the Latin ___*annus*___, meaning _year_.

9. To **locate** somewhere on a map is to find a place. The word comes from the Latin ___*locus*___, meaning _place_.

10. To **eject** someone is to throw that person out. The word comes from the Latin ___*jacere*___, meaning _to throw_.

13E Passage

Read the passage below; then complete the exercise that follows.

Anne Frank's Diary

Anne Frank was eleven years old in 1940 when the armies of Adolf Hitler, the Nazi ruler of Germany, **invaded** Holland, where she lived with her parents and her older sister. The Frank family was Jewish. They were **appalled** by Hitler's **fanatic** hatred of Jews and his plan to murder all the Jews in the countries he could control.

For two years, Anne Frank and her family lived in daily **terror** of being rounded up and taken away. Finally, the family, together with Anne's friend Peter and three others, went into hiding. Eight people **occupied** a tiny space hidden behind a bookshelf in Mr. Frank's office. They **depended** on brave friends who brought them food and news of the outside world. They hoped that Hitler would soon be defeated and their stay would be **temporary**, but after two more long years, they were still in hiding.

From 1942 to 1944, Anne Frank kept a diary in which she wrote about the things that happened every day and their **impact** on her life. Although life in these cramped surroundings was very **dreary**, Anne's diary is always interesting. In it she **reveals** her deepest thoughts and feelings. She complains of the feelings of **isolation** they all had, and she writes of their hopes of one day leading a normal life. No matter how **dejected** she felt, she always made the effort to keep the diary up-to-date.

Being discovered by the Germans was Anne Frank's greatest fear. Any unusual sounds from outside—slamming doors, heavy footsteps, German voices—could be a sign of danger. The little group had the use of a toilet, but they could not flush it during the day because someone in the building might hear it and **suspect** that people were hiding in that tiny space behind the bookshelves.

World War II ended in 1945, when Hitler's armies were **routed** in the East by the Russians and in the West by the Americans and the British. Sadly, its end came too late for Anne Frank. The Germans had found the family's hiding place the year before. Everyone was sent to Hitler's death camps, and it was in one of them, in March of 1945, two months before the end of the war in Europe, that Anne died. She was sixteen years old.

We would not know of her **tragic** story but for her diary. She left it behind when she was taken away, and her father, who managed to stay alive while in the Nazi death camp, discovered it when he returned home after the war. The diary was still there, in the place where his daughter had hidden it.

Answer each of the following questions in the form of a sentence. If a question does not contain a vocabulary word from this lesson's word list, use one in your answer. Use each word only once. Questions and answers will then contain all fifteen words (or forms of the words).

1. What part of Anne Frank's story had the greatest **impact** on you?

Hitler killed jews.

2. What terrible misfortune happened to the people of Holland in 1940?

Hitler and his army invaded Holland.

3. Why is Hitler such an **appalling** figure in the world's history?

He planed to murder all jews.

4. What was the main reason for Hitler's actions?

He had fanatic hatred of jews.

5. Why did the European Jews fear the Germans?

They terrified jews.

6. What is the meaning of **occupied** as it is used in the passage?

To live in.

7. How did Anne Frank's family and friends get food?

They depended on brave friends

8. Why did those in hiding think their stay might be **temporary**?

Hitler might of defeated Holland soon.

9. What might those in hiding have done to make life less **dreary**?

They hoped life will be normal.

10. Why do you think readers of her diary feel so close to Anne Frank?

They revealed her deepest thoughts. (reveal)

11. Why do you think those in hiding complained of feeling **isolated**?

They were not able to see places and people.

12. At what times do you think Anne Frank might have been most **dejected**?

When it was war.

13. What made it possible for the Frank group to stay hidden for two years?

They never suspected them because were quiet. (suspected)

14. What happened to Adolf Hitler's armies in 1945?

Russians routed them. (routed)

15. Why is Anne Frank's story such a **tragic** one?

Sad things happen.

FUN & FASCINATING FACTS

The word **deject** comes from the Latin roots *de*, meaning *away from*, and *jacere*, meaning *to throw*. Someone who is *dejected* is thrown, or cast down, in spirit. The word **project** (used as a verb) combines the Latin prefix *pro*, meaning *forward*, with *jacere*. To *project* something means to throw it forward or send it into space. A movie *projector* is a machine that throws an image onto a screen. Many other words are build from *jacere*, including **reject** (meaning *to throw away*), **inject** (meaning *to force, drive, or throw into something*), and **eject** (*to throw out*).

The lesson word **depend** comes from the Latin roots *de* and *dependēre*, meaning *to hang*. Something that is *impending* is something that is "hanging," or about to happen.

Lesson 14

Word List Study the definitions of the words below; then do the exercises for the lesson.

afford
ə fôrd´

v. 1. To be able to pay for.
Can you **afford** a new pair of running shoes?
2. To be able to do.
When you're on the soccer team, you can't **afford** to miss a night's sleep.
3. To give; to provide.
Music **affords** me much pleasure.

boast
bōst

v. 1. To talk with too much pride in oneself or in what one owns or has done; to brag.
Ben **boasted** about all the games he had won.
2. To have and to take a proper pride in having.
San Francisco **boasts** one of the finest bridges in the world, the Golden Gate Bridge.
n. An act of boasting.
"It was just a **boast**," Julio said. "I can't really run five miles."

chord
kôrd

n. Three or more notes of music played together.
Becca played a few **chords** on the guitar.

exceptional
ek sep´ shən əl

adj. Unusually good.
The batik cloth was of **exceptional** quality.

fortunate
fôr´ chə nət

adj. Lucky.
You are **fortunate** to have such kind friends.

fringe
frinj

n. 1. An edge made of short lengths of material such as thread, used to decorate clothes, curtains, etc.
My skirt had a **fringe** down the side.
2. An outside edge.
At the concert, I stood at the **fringe** of the crowd.

humble
hum´ bəl

adj. 1. Plain and simple.
Abraham Lincoln was raised in a **humble** log cabin.
2. Not proud; modest.
In her **humble** speech of thanks, the new mayor said she would need all the help she could get.
v. To bring down to defeat.
Our soccer team **humbled** Newton High with a score of seven goals to one.

meadow
me´ dō

n. A field of grass or wildflowers.
In the middle of the **meadow** stood a cow and its calf.

melancholy
me´ lən käl ē

adj. Filled with sorrow; very sad.
The movie was so sad it left me in a **melancholy** mood.
n. A state of sadness.
His **melancholy** began to affect my mood and I grew more and more dejected.

obstinate äb´ stə nət	*adj.* Not willing to give in; stubborn. You can't persuade him to do anything—he's too **obstinate**.
plead plēd	*v.* 1. To ask for something that is felt to be very important; to beg. The family **pleaded** with reporters to leave them alone. 2. To respond to a charge by a court of law. The prisoner said he wished to **plead** not guilty.
plunge plunj	*v.* 1. To throw oneself into. We **plunged** into the pool and swam a few laps. 2. To push or force quickly. I **plunged** the spade into the earth. 3. To drop sharply. The price of land near the new dump **plunged** last year. *n.* A sudden dive or fall. My spirits took a **plunge** when I saw the first page of the test.
relent ri lent´	*v.* To become less strict. My parents finally **relented** and said I could go to the concert.
submit sub mit´	*v.* 1. To give to someone to look over or decide about. Each student is asked to **submit** a picture for the yearbook. 2. To give in to someone or something. My sister was always telling me what to do, but I refused to **submit** to her.
trudge truj	*v.* To walk slowly and heavily, as though with great effort. We had to **trudge** through deep snow to reach the door.

14A Finding Meanings

Choose two phrases to form a sentence that correctly uses a word from Word List 14. Write each sentence in the space provided.

80

1. (a) Fortunate people   (c) are not vain.
   (b) Humble people   (d) change their minds easily.

Fortunate people are not vain.

2. (a) three or more notes played together.   (c) A plunge is
   (b) an edging of short lengths of material.   (d) A chord is

A chord is three or more notes played together.

3. (a) A fortunate person is one   (c) who suffers from poor health.
   (b) who is lucky.   (d) A melancholy person is one

A fortunate person is one who is lucky.

4. (a) A boast is
   (b) A meadow is
   (c) a grassy field.
   (d) a steep hill.

A meadow is a grassy field.

5. (a) beg for something.
   (b) deny something.
   (c) To plead is to
   (d) To submit is to

To plead is to beg for something.

6. (a) To boast a fine sports stadium
   (b) To afford a fine sports stadium
   (c) is to take good care of it.
   (d) is to take pride in it.

To boast a fine sports stadium is to take pride in it

7. (a) An exceptional student is one who
   (b) An obstinate student is one who
   (c) is very lucky.
   (d) has great ability.

An exeptional student is one who has great ability.

8. (a) a sharp drop.
   (b) a change of mind.
   (c) A plunge is
   (d) A fringe is

A plunge is a sharp drop.

9. (a) give it to someone for approval.
   (b) To afford something is to
   (c) To submit something is to
   (d) be ashamed of it.

To submit something is to give it to someone for approval.

10. (a) Obstinate people
    (b) Melancholy people
    (c) are unable to make up their minds.
    (d) are unwilling to change their minds.

Obstinate people are unable to make up their minds.

afford
boast
chord
exceptional
fortunate
fringe
humble
meadow
melancholy
obstinate
plead
plunge
relent
submit
trudge

14B Just the Right Word

Improve each of the following sentences by crossing out the bold phrase and replacing it with a word (or a form of the word) from Word List 14.

except

1. Raoul had no choice but to **give in** to his parents' rules.

plead

2. After you **say, when asked by the judge, that you are** not guilty, the trial will begin.

humble

3. Our first apartment was **plain and simple**, but we loved it.

boast

4. It was Aunt Oona's **proud claim** that she could run two miles in twelve minutes.

5. At first Mom said we couldn't ride our bikes to the movies, but after thinking it over she **changed her mind and said that we could**. *submitted*

6. Neema and Bill **walked slowly and with much effort** *trudged* up the steep path to the top of Corey Hill.

7. The crowd gasped as the Olympic swimmer **dived suddenly** *plunged* into the pool.

8. I prefer the tan lampshade with the **edge of short lengths of thread sewn on for decoration**. *fringe*

9. We were all wondering how Alisa could **spare the money for** *afford* all those new clothes.

10. The second movement of the Brahms symphony fills me with **feelings of great sadness**. *melancholy*

14C Applying Meanings

-3

Circle the letter of each correct answer to the questions below. A question may have more than one correct answer.

1. Which of the following might a person **boast** about?

   (a) cheating   (c) winning

   (b) losing   (d) failing

2. Which of the following might make a person feel **fortunate**?

   (a) having good health   (c) living in a free country

   (b) having kind parents   (d) getting free tickets to the circus

3. Which of the following might have a **fringe**?

   (a) a crowd   (c) a blanket

   (b) a lake   (d) a story

4. Which of the following might be too much for most people to **afford**?

   (a) to go on a trip around the world   (c) to miss a meal

   (b) to spare some time   (d) to buy a sports car

5. Which of the following can be **humble**?

   (a) a person   (c) a speech

   (b) a cottage   (d) a palace

6. Which of the following might you find in a **meadow**?

    (a) cows   (c) wildflowers

    (b) picnickers   (d) skyscrapers

7. Which of the following might a person **plead** for?

    (a) more help   (c) mercy

    (b) more money   (d) misfortune

8. Which of the following can **plunge**?

    (a) the temperature   (c) a rock

    (b) the price of a house   (d) the age of a house

14D Word Study

The suffix -*able* changes a verb into an adjective. Change each verb below into an adjective by adding this suffix to the word. Note that in words that end with the letters *y* or *e*, you must change the final letter to *i* before adding the suffix.

1. depend   *dependable*

2. vary   *variable*

3. remark   *remarkable*

4. prefer   *preferable*

5. afford   *affordable*

6. desire   *desireable*

The suffix -*ment* changes a verb to a noun. Change each verb below into a noun by adding this suffix to the word.

7. entertain   *entertainment*

8. replace   *replacement*

9. nourish   *nourishment*

10. equip   *equipment*

11. achieve   *achievement*

12. resent   *resentment*

afford
boast
chord
exceptional
fortunate
fringe
humble
meadow
melancholy
obstinate
plead
plunge
relent
submit
trudge

14E Passage

Read the passage below; then complete the exercise that follows.

How Water Lilies Began

This is a folktale from Wales, a small country west of England. It tells how water lilies came to grow in a lake in the Welsh mountains. It was all because of Huw, a farmer's son who loved to play the harp and never went to school. Huw lived with his mother in a **humble** cottage by the side of a mountain. Every morning, he drove his mother's black and white cows up the mountain, where they spent the day in a **meadow** by the side of the lake.

One day, Huw took his harp and played a few **chords** as he watched over the herd. To his astonishment, six silver cows rose out of the water, drawn by the music. Their coats gleamed in the sunlight as they gathered around Huw and listened to him play. They stayed with the herd all day, following the rest of the cows back to the farm that evening. Huw's mother felt very **fortunate** to have such fine new cows. She **boasted** to her neighbors that they gave twice as much milk as the black and white ones. And, she added, the milk was of **exceptional** quality.

All went well until one of the silver cows stopped giving milk. After waiting a few days, Huw's mother told the butcher to come the next day and take the cow away. Huw **pleaded** with his mother to spare the animal, but she wouldn't **relent**. She told Huw that they couldn't **afford** to have even one cow eating grass and giving nothing in return. The boy knew how **obstinate** his mother could be once her mind was made up, but he argued with her for as long as he dared. When his mother told him to be quiet, he knew he had no choice but to **submit** to her will.

The next morning, as he **trudged** up the mountain, Huw could think of nothing but the beautiful silver cow that was going to be sold. The music he played on his harp that day became increasingly **melancholy** until at last, his eyes filled with tears, he could play no more. He stood up and threw his harp into the lake. At once a strange thing happened. The six silver cows ran to the edge of the lake and **plunged** in. They were never seen again.

Soon masses of silver water lilies began to grow all along the **fringes** of the lake where the silver cows had jumped in. They still grow there today. Huw's mother died long ago, and Huw is now an old man. If you should meet him and tell him you don't believe this story, he will be happy to take you up the mountain and show you the beautiful silver water lilies.

Answer each of the following questions in the form of a sentence. If a question does not contain a vocabulary word from this lesson's word list, use one in your answer. Use each word only once. Questions and answers will then contain all fifteen words (or forms of the words).

1. Why might it be easy to pick the water lilies that grew in the lake?

They began to grow on the fringes of the lake.

2. How did the music Huw played match his mood?

He played melancholy music.

3. What is the meaning of **afford** as it is used in the passage?

It means they could not afford it.

4. How can you tell that Huw's family was not wealthy?

They lived a humble life.

5. How can you tell from the narrative that Huw's mother was not a shy person?

No because she always boasted.

6. Where did Huw and the cows go every day?

Huw went to the meadows.

7. What did the silver cows seem to be responding to?

The chords that Huw played.

8. Why was milk from the silver cows worth more than milk from the other cows?

The milk was of exceptional quality.

9. Why did Huw's mother feel **fortunate** to have the silver cows?

They were fine cows.

10. How can you tell from the passage that Huw was unwilling to defy his mother?

He had no choice but submit her will.

11. What did Huw do when his mother said the butcher would take the cow?

Huw pleaded to spare the animal.

12. Did Huw's mother agree to do what he asked?

She did not relent. th She

13. What does the word **trudged** suggest about Huw's feelings as he went up the mountain?

He went there slowly and heavily.

14. Why was it a waste of time for Huw to argue with his mother?

His mother was obstinate.

15. What was the last glimpse that Huw had of the silver cows?

The last glimpse that he had of the cow was they plunged.

FUN & FASCINATING FACTS

Chord has another meaning in addition to the one given. In geometry, a *chord* is a straight line joining any two points on a circle.

Chord and *cord* are homophones. *Cord* is thick string or twine. It is also a unit of measurement; a *cord* of firewood is a stack that measures eight feet by four feet by four feet.

In the Middle Ages, over five hundred years ago, people believed that the human body contained four different kinds of fluids, called *humors*. The four humors were blood, phlegm, yellow bile, and black bile. When these were in balance, a person was said to be in good humor; when they were out of balance, a person's mood was affected. Too much blood made a person *sanguine*, or cheerful (the Latin word for blood is *sanguis*). Too much phlegm made a person *phlegmatic*, or slow to respond. Too much yellow bile, called *choler*, made a person *choleric*, or angry. Too much black bile, called *melan choler* made a person **melancholy,** or unhappy.

Lesson 15

> **Word List** Study the definitions of the words below; then do the exercises for the lesson.

apparent
ə par´ ənt

adj. 1. Clear.
It's **apparent** that no one's home.
2. Seeming or appearing to be.
The **apparent** cause of increase in the price of lettuce was the spring freeze.

ban
ban

v. To forbid, especially by passing a law or making a rule.
The hospital **bans** children from visiting patients.
n. A law or rule that forbids something.
There is a **ban** on wearing hats in class.

concentrate
kän´ sən trāt

v. 1. To focus all one's thoughts or efforts on.
It's hard for me to **concentrate** on homework when I hear the kids outside.
2. To bring or come together in one place.
Factories were **concentrated** along the east side of the Harlem River.
concentration (kän sən trā´ shən) *n.* Giving total attention to something.
Don't sing! It ruins my **concentration**.
concentrated *adj.* Of increased strength or thickness.
For breakfast, mix one part of **concentrated** orange juice to three parts water.

concern
kən surn´

v. 1. To be about; to interest.
Homelessness is a subject that should **concern** everyone.
2. To trouble or worry.
My parents are **concerned** about my brother's health.
n. 1. Something that involves a person or people.
Health care is a big **concern** for most people.
2. A business organization.
After college she got a job with a banking **concern**.

consider
kən si´ dər

v. 1. To think about carefully.
Since my teaching job is a temporary one, it's time to **consider** what I should do next.
2. To take into account.
Please **consider** my feelings when you comment on the story I wrote.
3. To believe.
I may only be seventeen, but I **consider** myself an adult.

contrast
kən trast´

v. 1. To compare in order to show the differences.
Before deciding on the design for the new gym, we are going to **contrast** the two suggested plans.
2. To show differences when compared.
His actions **contrast** greatly with his words.
n. (kän´ trast) A difference.
Our new apartment is a welcome **contrast** to our old one.

fragile
fra´ jəl

adj. Easily broken or damaged.
This antique chair is so **fragile** that it would break if anyone sat on it.

menace
me´ nəs

n. Something that is likely to do harm or is regarded as dangerous.
Icebergs are a **menace** to ships in the North Atlantic.
v. To be a danger to; to put at risk.
The approaching hurricane **menaces** the entire South Carolina coast.

pounce
pouns

v. To swoop down on and seize.
The cat **pounced** on the mouse as soon as it ventured from its hole.

prompt
prämpt

adj. Quick; without too much time passing.
I sent a **prompt** reply to Ahmed's letter.
v. To cause to act.
Seeing ants all over the counter **prompted** me to spend the afternoon cleaning the kitchen.

recent
rē´ sənt

adj. Of a time just before the present.
The **recent** outbreak of measles resulted in the temporary closing of our school.

symbol
sim´ bəl

n. Something that stands for something else.
The dove is a **symbol** of peace.

talon
ta´ lən

n. The claw of a bird, usually one that kills animals for food.
The hawk clutched its victim firmly in its **talons**.

trophy
trō´ fē

n. Something, as a prize or award, given to show success in an activity.
The Heisman **trophy** is a top football honor.

widespread
wīd´ spred´

adj. 1. Spread or stretched out over a large area.
The **widespread** wings of the condor can reach ten feet from tip to tip.
2. Happening or found over a large area.
There was **widespread** frost last night.

15A Finding Meanings

Choose two phrases to form a sentence that correctly uses a word from Word List 15. Write each sentence in the space provided.

1. (a) total attention.
   (b) a lack of interest.
   (c) Concern is
   (d) Concentration is

Concentration is total attention.

2. (a) An apparent winner is
   (b) one who always wins.
   (c) A recent winner is
   (d) one who seems to have won.

An apparent winner is one who seems to have won

3. (a) A concern is
   (b) A symbol is
   (c) a business organization.
   (d) something that is likely to do harm.

A concern is a business organization.

4. (a) To concentrate things is to
   (b) become scarce.
   (c) To pounce is to
   (d) bring them together in one place.

To concentrate things is to bring them together in one place

5. (a) took place a short time ago.
   (b) A recent storm is one that
   (c) A widespread storm is one that
   (d) lasted for just a short time.

A recent storm is one that lasted for just a short time.

6. (a) A contrast is
   (b) an unintended result.
   (c) a rule that forbids something.
   (d) A ban is

A ban is a rule that forbids something

7. (a) To prompt something is
   (b) To menace something is
   (c) to be a danger to it.
   (d) to allow it to happen.

To menace something is to be a danger to it.

8. (a) to show how they differ.
   (b) To contrast two things is
   (c) To consider two things is
   (d) to prefer one over the other.

To contrast two things is to show how they differ

9. (a) found all over.
   (b) broken into pieces.
   (c) Something that is widespread is
   (d) Something that is fragile is

Something that is widespread is found all over

10. (a) To prompt something is to
    (b) take it into account.
    (c) To consider something is to
    (d) forbid it.

To consider something is to take it into account.

11. (a) A trophy is
    (b) A symbol is
    (c) something that stands for something else.
    (d) an animal's claw.

A symbol is something that stands for something else.

apparent
ban
concentrate
concern
consider
contrast
fragile
menace
pounce
prompt
recent
symbol
talon
trophy
widespread

15B Just the Right Word

Improve each of the following sentences by crossing out the bold phrase and replacing it with a word (or a form of the word) from Word List 15.

1. My grandmother's teacups are too ~~easily broken~~ *fragile* to use every day.

2. The kitten ~~leaped through the air and landed~~ *pounced* on the ball of yarn.

3. What ~~was the reason~~ *prompted* you to embrace the idea of becoming a writer?

4. The eagle's ~~sharp, curved claws~~ *talons* grasped the fish and lifted it out of the water.

5. Her golfing ~~award for victory~~ *trophy* was the thing she took great pride in.

6. Chapter 5 ~~points out the differences between~~ *contrasts* school life today and that of a century ago.

7. ~~Keep your mind only~~ *Concentrate* on your driving and forget about looking at the scenery.

8. Have you ~~given any thought to~~ *considered* trading in your old car for a new one?

9. My grandmother's future is a subject that ~~is of great interest to~~ *concerned* my parents.

15C Applying Meanings

Circle the letter of each correct answer to the questions below. A question may have more than one correct answer.

1. Which of the following is a **recent** event?
   (a) this morning's breakfast
   (c) last night's supper
   (b) your grandparents' wedding
   (d) your first day at school

2. Which of the following is **fragile**?
   (a) a baseball bat
   (c) a gold ring
   (b) a glass ornament
   (d) a tree limb

3. Which of the following might cause **concern**?
   (a) a toothache
   (c) a hurricane warning
   (b) rising prices
   (d) a furious customer

4. Which of the following could be a **menace** to drivers?
   (a) icy roads
   (c) speed limits
   (b) thick fog
   (d) seat belts

5. Which of the following might **pounce** on another animal?
   - (a) an elephant
   - (b) an eagle
   - (c) a tiger
   - (d) a mouse

6. Which of the following is a **symbol** of the United States?
   - (a) the stars and stripes
   - (b) the Statue of Liberty
   - (c) the bald eagle
   - (d) the Liberty bell

7. For which of the following might you be given a **trophy**?
   - (a) taking care of a little sister
   - (b) winning a tennis match
   - (c) catching the biggest fish
   - (d) catching a cold

8. Which of the following might do **widespread** damage?
   - (a) a flood
   - (b) a hurricane
   - (c) a leaky roof
   - (d) an earthquake

15D Word Study

The prefix *con-* or *com-* means "with" or "together."

Fill in the first set of blanks with the correct form of the prefix *con-* or *com-* for each word below, and fill in the second set with a word that completes the meaning. All except the last two words are from this or previous lessons.

1. __con__trast — to compare one thing __with__ another
2. __con__centrate — to bring or come __together__ in one place
3. __com__municate — to be in touch __with__
4. __com__plete — __with__ nothing missing
5. __con__cern — to have to do __with__
6. __con__fuse — to mix one thing up __with__ another
7. __con__sider — to think over __with__ care
8. __con__tract — to draw closer __together__
9. __com__plain — to find fault __with__
10. __con__nect — to join one thing __with__ another

apparent
ban
concentrate
concern
consider
contrast
fragile
menace
pounce
prompt
recent
symbol
talon
trophy
widespread

15E Passage

Read the passage below; then complete the exercise that follows.

The Fall and Rise of the Bald Eagle

For over two hundred years, the bald eagle has been the **symbol** of America, with the likeness of this powerful bird found on our coins and on the Great Seal of the United States. Two hundred years ago, bald eagles were found throughout North America, but by the 1970s, there were very few left outside of Alaska. The only creatures that **menace** the bald eagle are human beings. Why were there so few of these birds left? What are they like?

The bald eagle is a large, powerful bird that is not really bald. It gets its name from its white-feathered head, which **contrasts** strongly with the rest of its brown-feathered body. When it flies, it looks strong, powerful, and as if it is a master of the air. Its keen vision, great **talons**, and large, strongly hooked beak equip the bald eagle to live by hunting. In its search for small animals and fish, which form the greater part of its diet, it will sometimes **pounce** on a small lamb or piglet. Because of this, ranchers and farmers waged war on bald eagles for hundreds of years, killing them in large numbers. In addition, hunters shot them in order to have them stuffed as **trophies**.

In the 1950s, it became **apparent** that there was a sharp drop in the number of bald eagles. The reason for this was soon discovered. The eagles' eggs were **fragile** and broke easily, killing the young chicks inside. The cause of the thin shells remained unknown for a number of years. Finally, the mystery was solved by a scientist named Rachel Carson.

Rachel Carson was **concerned** about the use of pesticides, chemicals used to kill insects that damage crops. In 1962, she wrote a book called *Silent Spring* that showed how some chemicals were harming the nation's wildlife. The book explained the cause of the thin eagle shells: it was DDT, a pesticide that had been in **widespread** use in the United States for over ten years. DDT had become **concentrated** in lakes and streams. Once it was in the water, it poisoned fish. The DDT in the fish that the bald eagles ate caused the birds to lay eggs with thin shells that broke easily.

Rachel Carson hoped that Congress would act **promptly** to end the use of DDT and save the national bird. But it was not until 1973 that Congress passed a law **banning** the use of DDT. In the same year, it also passed a law that made it a crime to harm certain birds and animals, including the bald eagle, that were **considered** to be in danger.

Gradually, the bald eagle's numbers began increasing. A **recent** count revealed that there were over ten thousand pairs of bald eagles in the United States. In 2007, this grand bird was removed from the national list of animals in danger of dying out. Laws continue to protect the bald eagle, however, and it is still illegal to harm eagles and their eggs.

Answer each of the following questions in the form of a sentence. If a question does not contain a vocabulary word from this lesson's word list, use one in your answer. Use each word only once. Questions and answers will then contain all fifteen words (or forms of the words).

1. When would a farmer be most likely to kill a bald eagle?

When a eagle pounce on a lamb or pig the farmer would kill it

2. When did we find out that the bald eagle was in danger of dying out?

In 1950s it had become apparent that there was a drop of eagles

3. What was the reason for the drop in the number of bald eagles.

The eagles egg were fragile and broke easily killing the chicks inside.

4. Explain why this story of the bald eagle has a happy ending.

after many efforts to protect the birds. A recent count revealed that there were over ten million eagles.

5. Why did the bald eagle have good reason to fear human beings?

The bald eagle menance human beings. farmers want to kill them.

6. How does the bald eagle capture its food?

They use there talons to capture their prey.

7. How did Rachel Carson show her **concern** about what was happening to the nation's wildlife?

She wrote a book on chemicals that harm eagle

8. What happened to DDT after it had been sprayed on crops?

DDT had been concentrated on lakes and streams

9. Where was DDT used?

DDT was used widespread in the United States

10. What did some hunters do with the bald eagles they shot?

They stuffed them as trophies

11. What is the meaning of **considered** as it is used in the passage?

It means to think about it carefully.

12. Why was it important for Congress to act **promptly**?

They had to save the national bird

13. What did Congress finally do?

Congress passed a law banning the use of DDT

14. How did the bald eagle get its name?

Its white feathers contrasts with the brown feathers.

15. Why does a picture of the bald eagle appear on the Great Seal of the United States?

It's a symbol of the United States.

FUN & FASCINATING FACTS

When the Apollo astronauts returned to Earth, they brought back *fragments* of rocks from the moon. The word means "parts that are broken off," and comes from the Latin *fractus*, which means "broken." Several other English words are formed from this same Latin root. If you break a bone, you have a *fracture*. If you break down the number 1 into smaller parts, such as halves or quarters, you get *fractions*. Finally, something that is **fragile** is easily broken.

When a stage actor forgets the next line, which is every actor's nightmare, a person off to the side may **prompt** him or her by saying it aloud. The *prompter* must say the line loud enough for the actor to hear but not so loud that the audience hears. If the audience does hear the prompter, the play usually gets an unintended laugh.

A *cymbal* is a musical instrument; it is one of a pair of brass plates that are struck together to make a ringing sound. This word and **symbol** are homophones, words that sound alike but have different meanings and different spellings.

Lesson 16

Word List Study the definitions of the words below; then do the exercises for the lesson.

apt
apt

adj. 1. Suited to; fitting.
"The Stilt" was an **apt** nickname for seven-foot-one-inch basketball star Wilt Chamberlain.
2. Likely or almost certain.
I am **apt** to do better on Spanish tests if I make vocabulary cards to study.

blossom
blä´ səm

n. A flower.
The white orange **blossom** stands out against the dark-green foliage.
v. 1. To come into bloom.
Dogwood trees **blossom** in May.
2. To develop.
After two years of playing bit parts, she **blossomed** into a star of the Broadway stage.

bough
bou

n. A large branch or limb of a tree.
The **boughs** of the apple tree were heavy with fruit.

content
kən tent´

adj. Happy with what one has; satisfied.
Give me a good book and a comfortable armchair and I am **content**.
contentment *n.* A state of being satisfied and at peace.
After a delicious dinner and a hot bath, I relaxed in total **contentment**.

detest
di test´

v. To dislike strongly; to hate.
Many Germans **detested** Hitler, but were afraid to speak out.
detestable *adj.* Causing or deserving strong dislike.
His racist views are **detestable**.

dusk
dusk

n. The time at the end of the day just before dark.
The streetlights go on at **dusk**.

extinguish
ek stiŋ´ gwish

v. To put out, as a fire or a light.
The sign at the campsite said, "Before leaving, make sure you **extinguish** your campfire."

familiar
fa mil´ yər

adj. 1. Often seen or experienced; known.
I was happy to see a **familiar** face in the crowd.
2. Having a good knowledge of.
Dan read about it in the newspaper and is **familiar** with the case.

obtain
əb tān´

v. To gain or get by making an effort.
We were lucky to **obtain** tickets for the jazz concert because they sold out very quickly.

orchard
ôr´ chərd

n. A place where fruit trees grow.
Every fall my brother and I go to an **orchard** where you can pick your own apples.

practice
prak´ tis

v. 1. To say or do over and over in order to get better at something.
If you **practice** Spanish every day, you should be able to get along when you go to Mexico.
2. To do; carry on, perform.
He was raised from an early age to **practice** politeness.
3. To work at as a profession.
Aunt Marianna is licensed to **practice** law in both California and Nevada.
n. 1. A repeated action or usual way of doing something.
It's my mother's **practice** to swim thirty laps every morning.
2. The work of a profession.
The **practice** of medicine has recently undergone many changes.

prune
proon

v. To cut off branches.
We had to **prune** the shrubs so we could see out of the window.
n. A dried plum.
Elijah usually soaks the **prunes** overnight and serves them for breakfast.

stout
stout

adj. 1. Heavily built; thickset.
He used to be thin, but he grew **stout** as he got older.
2. Strong; not easily bent or broken.
The roof of the barn was supported by six **stout** posts.

threadbare
thred´ ber

adj. Shabby and worn-out.
The **threadbare** blankets on the bed failed to keep us warm during the night.

wander
wän´ dər

v. 1. To go from place to place with no plan or purpose in mind.
We **wandered** around downtown, waiting for the post office to open.
2. To slip easily off the subject; to fail to work in a normal way.
Luis tried to concentrate on his math homework, but his mind began to **wander**.

16A Finding Meanings

Choose two phrases to form a sentence that correctly uses a word from Word List 16. Write each sentence in the space provided.

78   −2

1. (a) A blossom is
   (b) A practice is
   (c) the work of a profession.
   (d) something that is done right the first time.

A practice is the work of a profession.

2. (a) A familiar person is one who is
   (b) A stout person is one who is
   (c) a close relative.
   (d) heavily built.

A familiar person who is a close relative.

3. (a) To extinguish a light is to
   (b) To obtain a light is to
   (c) put it out.
   (d) put a shade over it.

To extinguish a light is to put it out.

4. (a) To prune is to   (c) gather fruit.
   (b) travel aimlessly.   (d) To wander is to

To wander is to travel aimlessly

5. (a) whatever is inside something.   (c) Contentment is
   (b) the approach of darkness.   (d) Dusk is

Dusk is the approach of darkness

6. (a) An orchard is   (c) a flower.
   (b) A blossom is   (d) a piece of fruit.

A blossom is a flower

7. (a) is found after a search.   (c) Something that is detestable
   (b) Something that is apt   (d) deserves hate.

Something that is detestable deserves hate.

8. (a) get rid of it.   (c) To practice something is to
   (b) keep doing it.   (d) To obtain something is to

To obtain something is to keep doing it

9. (a) a type of dried fruit.   (c) A bough is
   (b) a place where fruit grows.   (d) A prune is

A prune is a type of dried fruit

apt
blossom
bough
content
detest
dusk
extinguish
familiar
obtain
orchard
practice
prune
stout
threadbare
wander

16B Just the Right Word

Improve each of the following sentences by crossing out the bold phrase and replacing it with a word (or a form of the word) from Word List 16.

1. I **strongly dislike** *detest* your taste in music.

2. As I crawled along the **branch of the tree**, *bough* it began to bend under my weight.

3. If I raise my grade to a B-plus, I will be **very satisfied**. *content*

4. After three nights without enough sleep, my mind began to **fail to work in a normal way**. *stout*

5. My cousin's farm includes a large **piece of land on which fruit trees are growing**. *orchard*

6. My favorite blue sweater is **shabby and worn out**, *threadbare* but I refuse to throw it away.

7. My piano teacher said that if I keep ~~playing that part over and over again~~, I'll have the whole piece memorized. *practicing*

8. Beginning skiers are ~~very likely~~ to fall many times while they are learning. *apt*

9. Gina is going to ~~get hold of~~ the equipment we need for the camping trip. *obtain*

10. Your face is ~~known to me~~, but I can't remember your name. *familiar*

11. When do the rose bushes start to ~~have flowers growing on them?~~ *blossom*

16C Applying Meanings

Circle the letter of each correct answer to the questions below. A question may have more than one correct answer.

1. Which of the following might be **stout**?
   - (a) a person
   - (b) a rope
   - (c) a walking stick
   - (d) a cobweb

2. Which of the following would grow in an **orchard**?
   - (a) pears
   - (b) a chord
   - (c) potatoes
   - (d) tomatoes

3. Which of the following happens at **dusk**?
   - (a) the stars begin to appear
   - (b) it gets darker
   - (c) the sun rises
   - (d) it gets cloudy

4. Which of the following can a person **obtain**?
   - (a) a car roof rack
   - (b) a car trip
   - (c) a phone number
   - (d) a phone call

5. Which of the following can be **pruned**?
   - (a) trees
   - (b) leaves
   - (c) flowers
   - (d) branches

6. Which of the following might bring you **contentment**?
   - (a) being with your family
   - (b) getting together with friends
   - (c) feeling concerned about your health
   - (d) missing an important date

7. Which of the following are **familiar** sights in the city?

(a) buses   (c) shoppers

(b) taxicabs   (d) police cars

8. Which of the following might **wander**?

(a) a train   (c) a person going for a long walk

(b) a lost child   (d) a person setting off for work

16D Word Study

Write the synonym of each word on the left on the line next to it. Choose from the words on the right, which are in a different order.

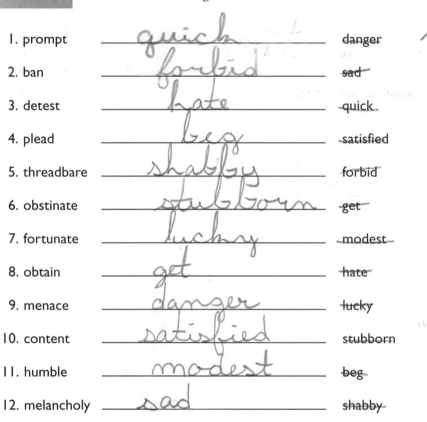

1. prompt	quick	danger	
2. ban	forbid	sad	
3. detest	hate	quick	
4. plead	beg	satisfied	
5. threadbare	shabby	forbid	
6. obstinate	stubborn	get	
7. fortunate	lucky	modest	
8. obtain	get	hate	
9. menace	danger	lucky	
10. content	satisfied	stubborn	
11. humble	modest	beg	
12. melancholy	sad	shabby	

apt
blossom
bough
content
detest
dusk
extinguish
familiar
obtain
orchard
practice
prune
stout
threadbare
wander

16E Passage

Read the passage below; then complete the exercise that follows.

The Story of Johnny Appleseed

In the late 1700s, most Americans had never tasted an apple. That's because very few apple trees grew outside of New England. A man named John Chapman did more than anyone else to change that. He enjoyed sinking his teeth into a sweet, juicy apple and wanted to share his enjoyment with others. For forty years, as he **wandered** through Ohio, Indiana, and western Pennsylvania, it was his **practice** to take a bag of apple seeds with him, planting them as he went along.

Chapman **obtained** the seeds from New England cider mills after the apples had been pressed for cider. Over the years, due entirely to his efforts, apple **orchards** were growing in many of the places he had visited. From time to time, he returned to them in order to **prune** the trees and make sure they stayed healthy.

This unusual man was born in Leominster, Massachusetts, and began his travels in 1797, when he was in his early twenties. When he needed money, he knew that just down the road there would be someone who would give him work and pay him a dollar or two. Chapman spent most days on the road, a **stout** walking stick cut from an apple tree in his hand and a tall, black hat on his head. At **dusk**, he looked for a place to spend the night. If there was no house with a room to offer him nearby, he was **content** to sleep under the stars. He had few needs, and it didn't bother him that his clothes were **threadbare**.

Because he **detested** killing of any kind, John Chapman refused to eat meat. Once he even **extinguished** a campfire because mosquitoes were flying into the flames and dying. He had no fear of wild animals, and they seemed to sense that he would do them no harm. In one of the many stories told about Chapman, he spent the night in the company of a friendly bear.

When he returned to places he had visited before, Chapman was greeted as an old friend. He loved to come back in the spring and see apple trees he had planted years before full of pink and white **blossoms**. But his greatest pleasure was to return in the fall to see their **boughs** weighed down with apples. Over the years he became a **familiar** sight to the people living on the farms and in the small towns of the Ohio River Valley. They gave him the very **apt** name we know him by today—Johnny Appleseed.

Answer each of the following questions in the form of a sentence. If a question does not contain a vocabulary word from this lesson's word list, use one in your answer. Use each word only once. Questions and answers will then contain all fifteen words (or forms of the words).

1. Why is Johnny Appleseed an **apt** name for John Chapman?

He was suited with his name.

2. Why did people have reason to be grateful to Chapman?

He brought apple orchards to the people.

3. How do we know Chapman was not vain about his appearance?

He had a few needs, and didn't bother that his clothes were threadbare.

4. Why did Chapman refuse to eat meat?

He detested the killing of animals.

5. How can we tell that John Chapman was not usually in a hurry? wander

For forty years he wandered through Ohio, Indiana, and Pennsylvania.

6. What is the meaning of **practice** as it is used in the passage?

To do it over and over until he got it right.

7. Where did Chapman get his apple seeds? obtained

He obtained seeds from new england.

8. What did Chapman look for in choosing something from which to make a walking stick? stout

He choose a stout.

9. What did Chapman do at the end of the day when he was traveling? dusk

At dusk he looked for a place to stay.

10. What did Chapman do if there was no one to give him a night's lodging? content

He was content to sleep under the stars.

11. Why did Chapman once put out his campfire? extinguished

He extinguished it because the bugs got dead in the fire.

12. What sight did Chapman enjoy in the spring?

He enjoyed blossoms.

13. Did the apple trees Chapman planted yield much fruit?

He had boughs of apples.

14. How do you know that Chapman often returned to places he had been to before?

It was familiar to him.

15. Why did Chapman return to places where he had planted trees? prune

He had to prune the trees.

FUN & FASCINATING FACTS

In Lesson 10, you learned that the word *orphan* comes from an old Sanskrit word. Another word that comes from this same language is **apt**. The Sanskrit word *apta* means "suitable" or "fitting." An *apt* remark is one that is a suitable or fitting thing to say.

In some languages, such as Russian, a word is pronounced the way it is spelled. That is not the case with English, which is one of the reasons English can be so difficult to learn. The word **bough**, for example, rhymes with *bow*. These two words are homophones. Imagine a person studying English who tries to read the following sentences, all of which contain words ending in *-ough*:

I have a bad *cough* (rhymes with *off*).
I've had *enough* (rhymes with *stuff*).
I'm coming *through* (rhymes with *shoe*).
Bread is made from *dough* (rhymes with *go*).

As an adjective, **content** means "satisfied." It can also be a noun, however, meaning "the amount contained." Then it is pronounced con' tent. (Water with a high lead *content* is unfit to drink.) The word is often used in its plural form, *contents*, and means "all that is contained." (The grocery bag split, spilling its *contents* onto the floor.)

Review for Lessons 13–16

roo

Crossword Puzzle Solve the crossword puzzle below by studying the clues and filling in the answer boxes. Clues followed by a number are definitions of words in Lessons 13 through 16. The number gives the word list in which the answer to the clue appears.

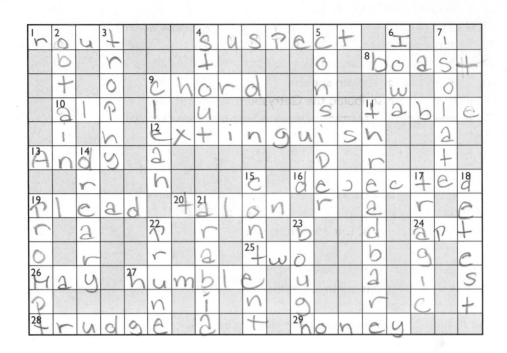

Clues Across

1. To defeat completely (13)
4. To believe without having proof (13)
8. To have and take pride in (14)
9. Several notes of music played together (14)
10. One of a group of mountains in Europe (13)
11. Chairs go around it.
12. To put out, as a fire or a light (16)
13. Short for "Andrew"
16. In low spirits (13)
19. To beg; to ask for something (14)
20. The claw of a bird that hunts small animals (15)
24. Suited to; fitting (16)
25. One, _____ , three
26. April, _____ , June
27. Not proud; modest (14)
28. To walk slowly and heavily (14)
29. It comes from bees.

Clues Down

2. To get by making an effort (16)
3. A prize or award (15)
4. Strong; not easily bent or broken (16)
5. To give careful thought to (15)
6. A state in the Midwest
7. To set apart (13)
9. Opposite of *dirty*
11. Shabby; worn out (16)
14. Lacking fun or excitement (13)
15. Satisfied with what one has (16)
17. Causing great sadness (13)
18. To dislike strongly (16)
19. Quick; without too much time passing (15)
21. Saudi _____ , a country in the Middle East
22. To cut off parts, especially branches (16)
23. A large branch of a tree (16)

Lesson 17

> ## Word List
Study the definitions of the words below; then do the exercises for the lesson.

address
ə dres´

v. 1. To direct one's words to.
The head of the honor society **addressed** the whole student body.
2. To apply oneself to something.
As soon as Ms. Lu finishes solving one problem, she has to **address** a new one.
n. 1. A written or spoken speech.
President Lincoln scribbled the Gettysbury **Address** on an envelope.
2. (a´ dres) The place where someone lives or receives mail.
Let the post office know if you change your **address.**

approve
ə pro͞ov´

v. To think well of; to agree to.
My friend Lucia **approved** my choice of a dress for the party.
approval   *n.* Thinking well of; agreeing to.
My parents' **approval** is important to me.

conclude
ən klo͞od´

v. 1. To bring or come to an end.
It took us at least ten minutes to reach the exit after the concert **concluded**.
2. To form an opinion.
Jan **concluded** that mowing lawns was the best way to earn money next summer.
conclusion   *n.* 1. The end.
A bow by the conductor marked the **conclusion** of the concert.
2. A judgment.
After talking to my teachers and my parents, I came to the **conclusion** that taking Spanish would be more useful to me than taking French.

deprive
di prīv´

v. To keep from having; to take away from.
The thunderstorm at 3:00 a.m. **deprived** me of a good night's sleep.

elder
el´ dər

n. 1. A person who is older.
Sometimes we can learn a lot from our **elders** just by observing the way they live their lives.
2. Someone people look up to because of age and experience.
The **elders** of the village met to decide what to do about the increasing number of tourists.
adj. Older.
My **elder** brother is a senior in high school.

escort
es kôrt´

v. To travel with; to guide or protect a person.
When her husband was away, Anna asked her brother to **escort** her to the play.
n. (es´ kôrt) One or more persons that escort.
The president always has a police **escort** when he travels by car.

fare
fer

n. 1. Money paid for a trip, by bus or train, for example.
What is the **fare** from Chicago to Orlando by air?
2. Food and drink.
The new restaurant serves Chinese **fare**.
v. To get along.
I wonder how my sister is **faring** on her mountain climbing trip.

forlorn fôr lôrn´	*adj.* Sad and lonely. Sam looked lost and **forlorn** as he sat waiting for his mother.

hearty
här´ tē

adj. 1. Healthy; strong.
Grandpa liked to boast that at the age of eighty-five, he still had a **hearty** appetite at every meal.
2. Satisfying and full of flavor; tasty.
The **hearty** vegetable chili hit the spot on a cold day.
3. Friendly and enthusiastic.
Uncle Pete gave a **hearty** chuckle when my little brother told a joke.

inhale
in hāl´

v. To breathe in.
I tried to catch my breath by **inhaling** deeply several times.

merit
me´ rit

v. To deserve.
The students' ideas for changes in the sports program **merit** careful study by the school board.
n. Good qualities; worth.
Dalal's teacher thought his fund-raising idea had **merit** and asked him to explain it to the class.
merits *n. pl.* The actual facts.
The judge said to forget what we'd heard on television and judge the case on its **merits**.

stingy
stin´ jē

adj. Not generous.
Azania is too **stingy** to share her candy with anyone.

summon
su´ mən

v. 1. To call or send for.
My father **summoned** me to the phone.
2. To call forth; to gather.
I **summoned** all my courage and walked out on the stage.

valiant
val´ yənt

adj. Full of courage; brave.
The firefighters were honored for their **valiant** deeds.

waft
wäft

v. To move or be moved lightly over water or air; to drift.
Petals from the cherry blossoms **wafted** over the path on the gentle breeze.

17A Finding Meanings

Choose two phrases to form a sentence that correctly uses a word from Word List 17. Write each sentence in the space provided.

1. (a) An address is
   (b) A fare is
   (c) the time spent alone.
   (d) the money charged for a trip.

A fare is the money charged for a trip

2. (a) breathe it in.
   (b) do without it.
   (c) To conclude something is to
   (d) To inhale something is to

To inhale something is to breathe it in.

3. (a) one that is enthusiastic.
   (b) one that shows agreement.
   (c) A forlorn expression is
   (d) A hearty laugh is

A hearty laugh is one that is enthusiastic.

4. (a) The conclusion of a play is
   (b) The merit of a play is
   (c) the beginning of it.
   (d) the end of it.

The conclusion of a play is the end of it.

5. (a) shun that person.
   (b) ask that person to come.
   (c) To deprive someone is to
   (d) To summon someone is to

To summon someone is to ask that person to come.

6. (a) to be worthy of it.
   (b) To merit something is
   (c) To be deprived of something is
   (d) to value it.

To merit something is to value it.

7. (a) A person's approval is
   (b) the place he lives.
   (c) A person's address is
   (d) a feeling of distrust.

A persons address is the place he lives.

8. (a) Someone who is forlorn
   (b) Someone who is valiant
   (c) feels good about the future.
   (d) feels sad and lonely.

Someone who is forlorn feels sad and lonely.

9. (a) a business partner.
   (b) An escort is
   (c) a wise, old person.
   (d) An elder is

An elder is a wise, old person

10. (a) A stingy person is
    (b) A valiant person is
    (c) one who is full of courage.
    (d) one who is generous.

A valiant person is one who is full of courage

17B Just the Right Word

Improve each of the following sentences by crossing out the bold phrase and replacing it with a word (or a form of the word) from Word List 17.

1. The smell of freshly-mown hay **was carried by the breeze** across the meadow. *wafted*

2. Trees that are **prevented from getting a supply** of proper nourishment will die. *deprived*

3. The New Town Inn boasts that it offers the finest **food and drink** at the lowest prices in town. *fare*

4. My **view, after thinking about all the issues**, is that no real harm was done.

conclusion

5. "Allow me to **stay beside you and walk with** you to your carriage," the gatekeeper said.

escort

6. Samantha cannot marry without her parents' **agreement that she is doing the right thing**.

approval

7. After such a **tasty and satisfying** meal, we all felt like taking naps.

hearty

8. They are so **unwilling to spend any more than they absolutely have to** that they expect me to babysit for fifty cents an hour.

stingy

9. The lawyer said that as long as the case is decided on the **facts as they are known**, her client will win.

merits

10. Mayor Coffey **made a few remarks to** the people gathered outside city hall, thanking them for their support.

summoned

17C Applying Meanings

Circle the letter of each correct answer to the questions below. A question may have more than one correct answer.

1. Which of the following can be **concluded**?
   - (a) a speech
   - (b) an agreement
   - (c) a meeting
   - (d) a project

address
approve
conclude
deprive
elder
escort
fare
forlorn
hearty
inhale
merit
stingy
summon
valiant
waft

2. Which of the following can **waft**?
   - (a) smoke
   - (b) smells
   - (c) stars
   - (d) hail

3. Which of the following can be **hearty**?
   - (a) a meal
   - (b) a greeting
   - (c) a storm
   - (d) an appetite

4. Which of the following show **approval**?
   - (a) turning thumbs down
   - (b) applauding
   - (c) cheering
   - (d) booing

5. Which of the following is a **valiant** act?
   - (a) giving up easily
   - (b) standing up for one's beliefs
   - (c) running away
   - (d) blaming someone else

6. Of which of the following can one be **deprived**?

    (a) one's freedom   (c) one's good name

    (b) one's rights   (d) one's business

7. Which of the following can be **addressed**?

    (a) a meeting   (c) a package

    (b) a person   (d) a nation

8. Which of the following can be **inhaled**?

    (a) air   (c) steam

    (b) food   (d) music

17D Word Study

Words that sound the same but have different meanings and spellings are called homophones. *To, too,* and *two* are homophones; so are *ate* and *eight.* The form of humor, called a pun, depends on homophones. Here's an example: Why is *six* afraid of *seven*? Answer: Because *seven eight* (ate) *nine.*

Decide which of each homophone pair best fits each sentence. Write the word in the blank.

hail/hale

1. The rain turned to _hail_ as the temperature fell.

2. He was over ninety, but looked as _hale_ as ever.

peer/pier

3. We joined the fishermen at the end of the _pier_

4. I had to stand on tiptoe to _peer_ into the room.

vain/vein

5. A _vein_ carries blood to the heart.

6. A _vain_ person loves to be flattered.

slay/sleigh

7. The warriors' plan was to _slay_ their enemies.

8. The _sleigh_ sped swiftly over the snow.

bore/boar

9. I used a drill to _bore_ the hole.

10. A male pig is called a _boar_.

fare/fair

11. The bus _fare_ to Hoboken is ten dollars.

12. The county _fair_ begins this Saturday.

chord/cord

13. Jonah played a _chord_ on his guitar.

14. We tied the bundle of wood with a length of _cord_.

bough/bow

15. Every _bough_ of the tree was full of apples.

16. The Japanese greet strangers with a polite _bow_.

17E Passage

Read the passage below; then complete the exercise that follows.

An African Folktale

Some folktales tell of **valiant** deeds performed by great heroes; an example is the Japanese story of Tokoyo and the sea monster. Others, like the Welsh tale of the silver cows and the water lilies, explain how things came to be. A third group tells how the weak and helpless defeat the strong and powerful. This does not always happen in real life, but it does happen in folktales, as in this East African story of the *maskini* and the *tajiri*.

Every evening, the *tajiri*, or rich man, sat down to a **hearty** meal prepared for him in his own kitchen. The food that was left over would have been enough to feed a whole family, but the *tajiri* was extremely **stingy**. The leftovers from his table went to fatten his pigs so that he would have the benefit of them later.

The *maskini*, or poor man, lived on simple **fare**. He owned a goat that gave him milk and cheese, but his evening meal was usually nothing more than a bowl of porridge. However, he had found a way to make it more enjoyable. He would eat his meal while hidden outside the *tajiri*'s kitchen, where wonderful smells came **wafting** through the open window. They made the *maskini*'s mouth water, so the simple porridge seemed like a feast.

One evening, the *tajiri* decided to take a walk in his garden in order to work up an appetite for dinner. He saw the *maskini* sitting outside the kitchen window. As the *tajiri* watched, he saw the *maskini* **inhale** deeply, and a blissful look come over his face. How dare he help himself to my smells, thought the *tajiri*, and he ordered his servants to seize the *maskini* and **escort** him to the village jail.

A few days later, the *maskini* was **summoned** before the court that met weekly in the village center, where the case would be decided on its **merits**. The *tajiri* explained that the smells from the kitchen belonged to him, and the *maskini* was **depriving** him of them. As payment, he demanded the *maskini*'s goat, which was the only thing he owned. When asked to respond, the *maskini*, looking very **forlorn**, could only stare at the ground and shuffle his feet, afraid to speak. The village **elders**, who had been hearing the case, now withdrew to the shade of a nearby baobab tree. After a brief discussion, the village chief came forward and **addressed** the crowd.

address

approve

conclude

deprive

elder

escort

fare

forlorn

hearty

inhale

merit

stingy

summon

valiant

waft

"The *maskini* did help himself to the smells from the *tajiri*'s kitchen," she said. "However, he did not receive any food from him. We have **concluded**, therefore, that the *tajiri* should not be given the goat. However, in fairness to him we believe he should have the right to smell the *maskini*'s goat whenever he wants."

The *tajiri* was furious and left without saying a word. But the people of the village **approved** the court's decision. They felt that justice had been done.

Answer each of the following questions in the form of a sentence. If a question does not contain a vocabulary word from this lesson's word list, use one in your answer. Use each word only once. Questions and answers will then contain all fifteen words (or forms of the words).

1. Did the *maskini* put up a **valiant** defense in the court?

Maskini did not defend the court.

2. What is the meaning of **hearty** as it is used in the passage?

It means it is very tasty.

3. The story says the *tajiri* was **stingy**. How does it show this?

He was not generous.

4. How did the *tajiri* **fare** when he went to court?

He got demanded to give his goat.

5. What would have happened if the kitchen window had been closed?

The smells wouldn't waft through the window.

6. How did the *tajiri* know that the *maskini* was enjoying the smells from the kitchen?

He inhaled the smell deeply.

7. Why did the *maskini* need an **escort**?

So he wouldn't escape from going into jail.

8. Did the *maskini* have to go to court?

Maskini did have to go to court

9. What does it mean to say the case would be decided on its **merits**?

It means it depends if he deserves it or not

10. Had the *maskini* taken anything from the *tajiri*?

He took away his goat.

11. Why do you think the *maskini* looked **forlorn**?

He was afraid and sad.

12. What sort of person might become one of the village **elders**?

If he is old and wise.

13. To whom did the chief direct her remarks?

He addressed it to the crowd.

14. What is the meaning of **concluded** as it is used in the passage?

It means to come to a end.

15. How might the crowd have shown that it **approved** of the court's decision?

They felt that justice had been done.

FUN & FASCINATING FACTS

President Lincoln gave a famous speech at Gettysburg in 1863 that begins, "Four score and seven years ago." Why do we refer to it as the Gettysburg **Address** rather than the Gettysburg Speech? One reason is that *address* suggests something grander and more important than a speech. Anyone can make a speech, but you have to be someone important and the occasion a special one for it to be called an address.

As an adjective, **elder** means "greater than another in age or seniority." If we refer to someone greatest in age or seniority, we use *eldest*. (I have an *elder* brother named Mark. He is not the *eldest*.) (Sheila is the *eldest* of seven children.) Note that *elder* and *eldest* are used only when referring to persons, but *older* and *oldest* can refer either to persons or things.

We turn many words into their opposites simply by changing the prefix. **Inhale** means "to breathe in." It is made up of the prefix *in-*, meaning "in" and the root formed from the Latin verb *halare*, meaning "to breathe." By knowing that the prefix *ex-* means "out," you can turn *inhale* into its opposite and make a word that means "to breathe out." What is that word?

Fare and *fair* are homophones. *Fair* is an adjective with several meanings and is also a noun, as visitors to a county *fair* know very well.

Lesson 18

Word List
Study the definitions of the words below; then do the exercises for the lesson.

abreast
ə brest´
adj. or *adv.* 1. Side-by-side.
We walked three **abreast**, except where the path was so narrow that we had to walk single file.
2. Up-to-date.
I try to stay **abreast** of what is happening in the world by reading the paper every day.

barrier
bar´ ē ər
n. Anything that stops progress or blocks the way.
Lack of education is often a **barrier** to success in life.

breadth
bredth
n. 1. The distance of something from side to side; width.
The arrow missed the target by no more than a hand's **breadth**.
2. Wide range; largeness.
Carlos got the job because of his **breadth** of experience.

capital
ka´ pə tl
n. 1. Wealth that can be used to produce more wealth.
You don't need much **capital** to buy that pizza business.
2. The city where the government of a state or country is located.
The **capital** of Montana is Helena.
adj. Punishable by death.
Murder is a **capital** crime in many states.

ensure
in shoor´
v. To make sure or certain.
Wearing a seat belt will help **ensure** your safety in case of an accident.

external
ek stʉr´ nəl
adj. On or related to the outside.
The **external** walls of the house are covered with shingles as protection.

feud
fyo͞od
n. A long, bitter quarrel, especially one between two families.
It took the tragic deaths of Romeo and Juliet to end the **feud** between their two families.
v. To be enemies, to quarrel.
The Hatfields and the McCoys **feuded** for years.

fortress
fôr´ trəs
n. A building with strong walls made to be defended against attack; a fort.
Rather than attack the **fortress** directly, the invaders went around it.

frequent
frē´ kwənt
adj. Happening often or over and over.
My mother's business requires her to make **frequent** visits to Japan.
v. To go to over and over.
We **frequent** the local bakery regularly for oatmeal cookies.
frequency *n.* Number of times something is repeated.
My clarinet playing improved with the **frequency** of my practicing.

frontier
frun tīr´

n. 1. The line between two countries.
We said goodbye to France and crossed the **frontier** into Spain in the early morning.
2. The outer limits of the settled part of a country.
The American **frontier** moved slowly westward in the nineteenth century.
3. The outer limits of knowledge.
The **frontiers** of medicine are being pushed back at a rapidly increasing rate.

peasant
pez´ ənt

n. A person who makes a living from working the soil, especially in poorer countries.
The **Peasants'** Revolt in England in 1381 was a shock to the government.

petty
pe´ tē

adj. 1. Of little importance; small.
A **petty** disagreement over a parking space led to a bitter quarrel between them.

threat
thret

n. A warning that one may do harm.
Olivia tried to quiet her dog after her neighbor's **threat** to call the police.
threaten   *v.* To make a threat.
My brother **threatened** to tell my mother that I ate all the cake.
threatening   *adj.* Suggesting harm or danger.
The dark clouds looked very **threatening**.

utilize
yōō´ tl īz

v. To put to use.
We **utilized** whatever scraps of fabric we had to make a costume.

vast
vast

adj. Very great in area or amount.
The Pacific Ocean is a **vast** body of water.

18A Finding Meanings

Choose two phrases to form a sentence that correctly uses a word from Word List 18. Write each sentence in the space provided.

abreast
barrier
breadth
capital
ensure
external
feud
fortress
frequent
frontier
peasant
petty
threat
utilize
vast

1. (a) The breadth of something is
   (b) the number of times it occurs.
   (c) The frequency of something is
   (d) its unexpected absence.

The frequency of something is the number of time it occures.

2. (a) A frontier is
   (b) A barrier is
   (c) a person who makes a living from the soil.
   (d) the outer limits of the settled part of a country.

A frontier is the outer limits of a settled part of a cou ntry

3. (a) Capital is
   (b) severe punishment.
   (c) Breadth is
   (d) distance from side to side.

Breadth is distance from side to side

4. (a) to have knowledge of it.
   (b) to avoid it.
   (c) To be abreast of something is
   (d) To ensure something is

To abreast something is to have knowlage of it.

5. (a) is punishable by death.   (c) A petty crime is one that
   (b) goes unpunished.   (d) A capital crime is one that

A capitol crime is one that is punishable by death.

6. (a) something that blocks the way.   (c) A peasant is
   (b) something that can be used.   (d) A barrier is

A barrier is something that blocks the way.

7. (a) A vast army   (c) is one that has been routed.
   (b) is one about to attack.   (d) A threatening army

A threatning army is one about to attack.

8. (a) A fortress is   (c) a person who makes a living from the soil.
   (b) A peasant is   (d) a humble cottage.

A peasant is a person who makes a living from the soil.

9. (a) A petty difference is   (c) one that keeps increasing.
   (b) one of little importance.   (d) A vast difference is

A petty difference is one of little importance.

10. (a) A fortress is   (c) A feud is
    (b) a bitter quarrel.   (d) the line between two countries.

A feud is a bitter quarrel.

11. (a) make sure it happens.   (c) To ensure something is to
    (b) make sure it doesn't happen.   (d) To utilize something is to

To ensure something is to make sure it happens.

18B Just the Right Word

Improve each of the following sentences by crossing out the bold phrase and replacing it with a word (or a form of the word) from Word List 18.

1. My father ~~puts to good use~~ *utilizes* every leftover when he makes a casserole.

2. A ~~building that is made to be defended against attack~~ *fortress* should be built on high ground.

3. A country needs ~~wealth that can be used to produce more wealth~~ *capitol* in order to produce jobs.

4. The points Eric raised were so ~~lacking in importance~~ *petty* that everyone ignored them.

5. If you try to ~~suggest that you could be a danger to~~ *threaten* me, I won't talk to you any more.

6. I know most of the people who **make regular visits to** ~~the~~ Cosy Cafe; I have lunch there every day.

frequent

7. Most streets aren't wide enough for three cyclists riding **side by side.**

abreast

8. The land of the former Soviet Union is so **great in the area it covers** that it crosses nine time zones.

vast

9. The first symptoms of measles are **on the outside and show up on the skin.**

external

10. Many of the **lines separating the various countries** of Europe were redrawn after the First World War.

frontier

11. The two families continued to **keep up the long and bitter quarrel** because neither side was willing to give in.

feud

18C Applying Meanings

Circle the letter of each correct answer to the questions below. A question may have more than one correct answer.

1. Which of the following has **breadth**?
   - (a) a surface
   - (b) a point where lines meet
   - (c) a brick
   - (d) a line joining two points

2. Which of the following is an **external** symptom?
   - (a) a sore throat
   - (b) a stomach ache
   - (c) a skin rash
   - (d) a twitching eyelid

3. In which of the following places are you likely to find a **peasant**?
   - (a) a city
   - (b) a farm
   - (c) an office
   - (d) a field

4. Which of the following is a **threatening** remark?
   - (a) "See you later."
   - (b) "I'll get even with you!"
   - (c) "You'll be sorry."
   - (d) "I'm sorry."

5. Which of the following would be considered **vast**?
   - (a) the Atlantic Ocean
   - (b) the distance to the nearest star
   - (c) the universe
   - (d) the American prairie

abreast

barrier

breadth

capital

ensure

external

feud

fortress

frequent

frontier

peasant

petty

threat

utilize

vast

6. Which of the following is a **capital**?

(a) Washington, D.C. (c) Ottawa, Canada

(b) Paris, France (d) Bronx, New York

7. Which of the following are **petty** concerns?

(a) your choice of breakfast cereal (c) a broken fingernail

(b) your choice of school (d) a broken leg

8. Which of the following do people change **frequently**?

(a) their date of birth (c) their eating habits

(b) their socks (d) their names

18D Word Study

Write the antonym of each word on the left in the space next to it. Choose from the words on the right, which are in a different order.

1. stingy — generous — cowardly

2. familiar — strange — generous

3. approve — resist — start

4. stout — fragile — blissful

5. frequent — rare — resist

6. extinguish — light — exciting

7. submit — reject — tiny

8. conclude — start — reject

9. dreary — exciting — light

10. valiant — cowardly — fragile

11. vast — tiny — strange

12. forlorn — blissful — rare

18E Passage

Read the passage below; then complete the exercise that follows.

The Great Wall of China

Most visitors to China make a point of seeing the Great Wall. It is hard to miss because of its enormous size. It is about twenty-five feet high, and its **breadth** at the top is nearly twenty feet, wide enough for ten people to walk **abreast**. It starts in Gansu province in the south and ends at the Yellow Sea in the northeast, a distance of fifteen hundred miles. The part of the wall tourists visit most **frequently** goes from Beijing, the **capital** of China, to the Yellow Sea.

The Great Wall of China was built more than two thousand years ago as a **barrier** against tribes from the north. The person responsible for having it built was Shi Huang-ti, known as "the First Emperor of China." Before the country was united under his leadership, China was divided into a large number of **petty** kingdoms, ruled by local warlords who spent most of their time **feuding** among themselves. By the year 221 B.C., Shi Huang-ti had taken control of the whole country and made himself emperor.

Because the empire was so **vast**, it was not easy to defend. Shi Huang-ti had nothing to fear at home, but he worried about **external** attacks, especially from the north, where tribes from central Asia **threatened** his rule. To **ensure** the safety of his empire, he had the Great Wall built along China's northern **frontier.** It had watchtowers every few miles, as well as **fortresses** where the emperor's soldiers were housed, ready to fight off attacks. Building began in 214 B.C., and later rulers of China added to it in the west and south. Work on the wall was still being carried out four centuries ago.

Hundreds of thousands of Chinese **peasants** were forced to leave their farms to do the actual work of building the Great Wall. Everything had to be carried on the workers' backs or slung on poles because the wheelbarrow had not yet been invented. The builders **utilized** whatever was close at hand—blocks of stone in mountain areas and timber from forests. In other places, they used earth or sand mixed with twigs and reeds. Later on, bricks and tiles were used.

Shi Huang-ti is an important figure in Chinese history. He improved the workings of government and ordered the building of roads and canals to improve communications throughout the empire. He built a magnificent palace as well as many other fine public buildings. But his greatest achievement, and the thing for which he is remembered, is the Great Wall of China.

abreast
barrier
breadth
capital
ensure
external
feud
fortress
frequent
frontier
peasant
petty
threat
utilize
vast

Answer each of the following questions in the form of a sentence. If a question does not contain a vocabulary word from this lesson's word list, use one in your answer. Use each word only once. Questions and answers will then contain all fifteen words (or forms of the words).

1. Why do you think tourists visit the Great Wall so **frequently**?

It is just a magnificent place.

2. Why does it take a very long time to cross China?

It is only enough for ten people to walk abreast

3. Why would you expect to find many government offices in Beijing?

Beijing is the capitol of China.

4. Why did the "First Emperor" build the Great Wall?

To ensure the saftey of his empire.

5. What enemies was Shi Huang-ti worried about?

He worried about the northern tribes who threatened the rules.

6. How did the local warlords get along with each other?

They spent most of the time feuding themselves.

7. How much influence do you think the ruler of a **petty** kingdom would have?

They would have a little amount of influence.

8. Why was Shi Huang-ti concerned about the tribes in Central Asia?

He was worried about the external attacks from Central Asia.

9. Where would an invasion of China by the northern tribes have taken place?

It would be at China's Northern frontier.

10. What materials did the builders of the wall use?

They utilized whatever that was close in hand.

11. What was the purpose of the **fortresses** that were built into the wall?

It was where the soldiers were housed and ready to attack.

12. Why was it possible to use the top of the Great Wall as a road?

It was vast to build a road.

13. Why would the Great Wall be easy to see from the air?

It's breadth at the top is nearly twenty feet.

14. Why might the **peasants** have resented having to work on the wall?

They were forced to.

15. Was the Great Wall successful in doing what it was suppose to do?

The Great Wall of china was built years and years ago as a barrier.

FUN & FASCINATING FACTS

Don't confuse the word **capital**, which has several meanings as an adjective and is also a noun, with the word *capitol,* which is a noun only.

The *Capitol* (with an uppercase *C*) is the building in which the United States Congress meets. A *capitol* (with a lowercase *c*) is the building in which the governing body of a state meets. It might help you to remember the difference between *capital* and *capitol* if you note that most *capitols* are buildings with *domes,* a word with an *o* in it.

External refers to that which is outside, rather than inside. Its antonym, *internal,* refers to that which is inside rather than outside. The skin is the body's only *external* organ. The heart, lungs, liver, and kidneys are *internal* organs.

A related word to *external* is *exterior;* its antonym is *interior.* An *exterior* door is one on the outside; an interior door is one inside a building that connects one room with another.

Lesson 19

Word List
Study the definitions of the words below; then do the exercises for the lesson.

audition
ô dish´ ən

n. A short performance by an actor or musician as a test for a particular job.
Auditions for the school band will be held tomorrow.
v. To try out for.
Six people **auditioned** for the part of Helen Keller in the fourth-grade play.

create
krē āt´

v. To bring into being; to produce for the first time.
The computer industry has **created** many new jobs.
creative *adj.* Having new and original ideas.
Mozart was one of the most **creative** musicians that ever lived.
creation *n.* The act of bringing into being; something created.
The **creation** of three new teaching positions means that classrooms will be less crowded.

elevate
e´ lə vāt

v. To lift up; to raise to a higher level.
Jane Austen **elevated** the English novel to new heights.
elevation (ev lə vā´ shən) *n.* Height.
I have to look up the **elevation** of Mt. Monadnock for my chart.

eliminate
i li´ mə nāt

v. To get rid of; to remove or leave out.
Zeb decided to **eliminate** the last paragraph because his report was too long.
elimination (i li mə na´ shən) *n.* A getting rid of.
The **elimination** of the Red Sox from the pennant race upset my mother terribly.

engage
in gāj´

v. 1. To put to work; to hire.
The Beachfront Restaurant **engages** extra help every summer.
2. To keep busy or active.
Wen Lin tried to **engage** her cousin in conversation, but she was very shy.
3. To bind oneself to do something, especially to marry.
My parents got **engaged** on New Year's Eve.

entrance
in trans´

v. To fill with joy or delight.
The young dancers **entranced** the audience with their grace and beauty.
entrancing *adj.* Delightful.
The songs were so **entrancing** that we hated to see the performance end.

essential
e sen´ shəl

adj. Most important; very necessary.
Fresh fruit and vegetables are **essential** to a good diet.
essentials *n. pl.* Something that cannot be done without.
I packed my overnight bag with my toothbrush and other **essentials**.

foremost
fôr´ mōst

adj. First in importance, time, or place.
This new play by America's **foremost** playwright is breaking all box office records.

forsake fôr sāk´	*v.* To have nothing more to do with; to turn one's back on. I'd never **forsake** my old friends if I became rich and famous.
recognize re´ kig nīz	*v.* 1. To know and remember upon seeing. I **recognized** the name, but not the face. 2. To admit the truth or accept the existence of. For many years, the U.S. was unwilling to **recognize** the government of China. 3. To accept and approve. The manager told my mother that the company **recognizes** the good job she does.
sentimental sen tə men´tl	*adj.* Expressing feelings of love or pity, sometimes to excess. The movie was so **sentimental** that everyone was in tears.
source sôrs	*n.* The thing or place from which something comes. We decided to go on a trip to reach the **source** of the Nile River.
tour toor	*n.* A trip or journey in which one usually returns to the starting point. The band played over twenty concerts on its **tour** of the Midwest. *v.* To travel to different places. My cousin Anna and I **toured** the old part of Montreal in a horse-drawn carriage.
tradition trə dish´ən	*n.* A belief, custom, or usual way of doing things, handed down within families or other groups. Fireworks on July 4 are an American **tradition**. **traditional** *adj.* Handed down from age to age. My whole family enjoys getting together for a **traditional** Passover seder.
trio trē´ ō	*n.* A group of three people. Luis plays the cello in a **trio**.

audition
create
elevate
eliminate
engage
entrance
essential
foremost
forsake
recognize
sentimental
source
tour
tradition
trio

19A Finding Meanings

Choose two phrases to form a sentence that correctly uses a word from Word List 19. Write each sentence in the space provided.

1. (a) the things that are left out.
   (b) Traditions are
   (c) Essentials are
   (d) the things considered necessary.

2. (a) know or remember it.
   (b) To recognize a piece of work is to
   (c) To create a piece of work is to
   (d) make changes in it.

3. (a) passed down over time.
   (b) A traditional custom is one
   (c) that is no longer practiced.
   (d) A sentimental custom is one

4. (a) A creation is
   (b) A tour is
   (c) a small group.
   (d) something produced for the first time.

5. (a) to consider.
   (b) To entrance is
   (c) to delight.
   (d) To audition is

6. (a) turn one's back on that person.
   (b) protect that person.
   (c) To engage someone is to
   (d) To forsake someone is to

7. (a) Elimination of something is
   (b) finding a new and different use for it.
   (c) Elevation of something is
   (d) getting rid of it.

8. (a) To audition someone is to
   (b) To engage someone is to
   (c) hire that person.
   (d) get rid of that person.

9. (a) a journey around a place.
   (b) the answer to a puzzle.
   (c) A source is
   (d) A tour is

19B Just the Right Word

Improve each of the following sentences by crossing out the bold phrase and replacing it with a word (or a form of the word) from Word List 19.

1. Stephen Hawking is one of the world's **greatest and most important** experts on black holes. *foremost*

2. At my parents' anniversary party a **group of three singers** sang popular songs from the forties and fifties. *trio*

3. We were able to locate the **place that was the beginning** of the river by following it and hiking up to the mountains. *source*

4. The Pied Piper's job was to **get rid of** the rats from the town of Hamelin. *eliminate*

5. My cousin Becca and Juan Morales, her friend from grade school, became **promised to each other in marriage** on June 1. *engage*

6. Because I am so short, I have to **put at a higher level** every piano stool I sit on. *elevate*

7. I always cry at weddings because I'm so **easily affected by romantic feelings**. *sentimental*

8. Sequoya **brought into being for the first time** a written language for the Cherokee people. *created*

9. The government **admits the existence of** the need for laws to protect the wetlands. *recognize*

10. The **short performances that people gave who were trying out** for places in the orchestra lasted all day. *auditions*

11. We returned again and again to Trinidad because it is such a(n) **delightful and pleasurable** island. *entrancing*

19C Applying Meanings

Circle the letter of each correct answer to the questions below.
A question may have more than one correct answer.

1. Which of the following might one **audition** for?
   - (a) a job with a band
   - (b) an apartment rental
   - (c) a part in a play
   - (d) a factory position

2. Which of the following is **essential** for college?
   - (a) graduation from high school
   - (b) being on a sports team
   - (c) a birth certificate
   - (d) good grades

3. Which of the following are birthday **traditions**?
   - (a) blowing out candles
   - (b) having cake
   - (c) getting presents
   - (d) making pumpkin pie

4. Which of the following might one **tour**?
   - (a) a precipice
   - (b) a museum
   - (c) an address
   - (d) a film studio

5. Which of the following might one **forsake**?
   - (a) one's friends
   - (b) one's family
   - (c) one's career
   - (d) one's health

6. Which of the following might **elevate** one's spirits?
   - (a) being hailed by a friend
   - (b) a pessimistic remark
   - (c) being jeered by a crowd
   - (d) finishing a lot of work

audition

create

elevate

eliminate

engage

entrance

essential

foremost

forsake

recognize

sentimental

source

tour

tradition

trio

7. Which of the following might **entrance** a child?

(a) a red balloon

(c) a funny clown

(b) a melancholy tale

(d) a threatening gesture

8. Which should one **eliminate** for good health?

(a) a balanced diet

(c) eating fatty foods

(b) regular check-ups

(d) exercise

19D Word Study

The prefix *tri-* means "three" and comes from both Greek and Latin. A *triceratops* is a large, three-horned dinosaur. The letters *tri* at the beginning of a word do not always function as a prefix. Sometimes a word just happens to begin with these three letters.

Look at each word and its meaning below and decide if *tri* is a prefix. If it is, underline the first three letters. If it isn't, don't underline anything.

1.	triangle	a figure with three straight sides
2.	trillion	a thousand billion
3.	triplets	three babies born at a single birth
4.	trial	a case heard in a court of law
5.	tricycle	a child's bike with three wheels
6	trident	a three-pointed spear
7.	tricolor	the red, white, and blue French flag
8.	trio	a group of three
9.	tribe	a group of families ruled by a chief
10.	triplicate	made in three copies
11.	tripod	a three-legged stand
12.	trickle	to flow slowly in a thin stream

Read the passage below; then complete the exercise that follows.

Martha Graham—Artist and Teacher

Martha Graham was one of the **foremost** dancers of the twentieth century. She founded a dance company that performed modern dance for an ever-widening audience and was **recognized** as one of modern dance's greatest teachers.

Before Martha Graham's time, dance as a serious art form meant French and Russian ballet, which had remained largely unchanged since the nineteenth century. It told stories that were often **sentimental** and far removed from the real world, and followed fixed patterns of movement. Female dancers wore **traditional** tight-waisted costumes with short skirts, tights, and stiffened ballet shoes that enabled them to dance on their toes. Music was usually classical, often written especially for the ballet.

Martha Graham began by **eliminating** from her dances everything that she felt was unnecessary. What remained was a new kind of dance, stripped to its **essentials** with bare stage settings and the simplest of costumes. Her dancers were usually barefoot and wore loose, flowing clothes. Her subjects were drawn from a great variety of **sources** that included Native American life, scenes from American history, and the poetry of Emily Dickinson. She tried to develop a kind of dance that expressed human feelings as well as told a story.

Martha Graham's lifelong interest in dance began in 1912 when, at the age of seventeen, she saw Ruth St. Denis perform in San Francisco as part of her American **tour**. St. Denis was heavily influenced by Japanese, Indian, and Spanish dances, and Graham was **entranced** by what she saw. She began taking dancing lessons, and when she was twenty-two, she successfully **auditioned** for the Denishawn dance company, run by Ruth St. Denis and her husband, Ted Shawn. Graham stayed with the company for seven years and became one of its leading dancers.

In 1924, Martha Graham decided temporarily to **forsake** the life of a performer to concentrate on teaching and developing her own style of dancing. She returned to the New York stage two years later with a **trio** of female dancers formed from her best students; in 1930 she formed the much larger Martha Graham Dance Company. She preferred women dancers; not until 1938 did she **engage** male dancers to appear on stage with her. "Modern dance," she once said, "isn't anything in my mind except one thing—the freedom of women in America."

Her last public performance took place in 1969, when she was seventy-four years old. She had won over all her critics and had **elevated** modern dance to a new American art form. When she died in 1991, at the age of ninety-six, she was at work **creating** a new dance for her company. That unfinished work, *The Eyes of the Goddess*, was performed by her company shortly after her death as a tribute to one of America's greatest artists.

audition
create
elevate
eliminate
engage
entrance
essential
foremost
forsake
recognize
sentimental
source
tour
tradition
trio

Answer each of the following questions in the form of a sentence. If a question does not contain a vocabulary word from this lesson's word list, use one in your answer. Use each word only once. Questions and answers will then contain all fifteen words (or forms of the words).

1. How do people around the country get to see dance companies?

2. How did Martha Graham change the style of dance?

3. What were **traditional** costumes like?

4. How would you describe the Martha Graham stage?

5. What were French and Russian ballet like?

6. Where did Martha Graham get ideas for her dances?

7. How did Martha Graham feel about Ruth St. Denis's performance?

8. Why did Martha Graham **forsake** performing in 1924?

9. What is the meaning of **engage** as it is used in the passage?

10. How many other dancers did Martha Graham need to perform with her as a trio?

11. What is the meaning of **recognized** as it is used in the passage?

_____

12. What was Martha Graham doing at the time of her death?

_____

13. What does the passage say was Martha Graham's greatest achievement?

_____

14. Why is Martha Graham famous?

_____

15. What do you have to do to get into a dance company?

_____

FUN & FASCINATING FACTS

If you **audition** for a part in a play, you want to make sure that you are _heard_. The word itself suggests this; it comes from the Latin verb _audire_, which means "to hear." Other words formed from this root include the following:

Audible, loud enough to be heard (an _audible_ whisper);

Audio, intended to be heard (an _audio_ tape);

Audience, a group of people gathered together to hear (and also to see) whatever is being performed for their enjoyment;

Auditorium, a large room in which people come together to hear a presentation;

Auditory, having to do with the ear (the _auditory_ nerve).

A **trio** is a group of three, especially a group of three musicians or other entertainers. The word comes from the Latin (and Greek) word for "three." Other Latin numbers give us the following: _duet,_ two performers or a piece to be performed by two persons, from the Latin _duo; quartet,_ a group of four, from the Latin _quattuor; quintet,_ a group of five, from the Latin _quintus; sextet,_ a group of six, from the Latin _sex; septet,_ a group of seven, from the Latin _septem;_ and _octet,_ a group of eight, from the Latin _octo._

Entrance has two pronunciations: en 'transs, and 'en transs. The more common pronunciation, 'en transs, means _a way to go inside someplace or something._ En 'transs, _to fill with joy or delight,_ which appears in this lesson, is less common.

Lesson 20

▶ **Word List** Study the definitions of the words below; then do the exercises for the lesson.

arrest
ə rest´

v. 1. To stop the movement or progress of.
The doctors were able to **arrest** the spread of the disease.
2. To seize and charge with breaking the law.
When the police **arrested** the suspect, they found the stolen jewelry in his pocket!
n. The act of arresting.
The police officer made the **arrest** at the scene of the crime.

capable
kā´ pə bəl

adj. Able to do things well; skilled.
Although she is only fourteen, Samantha is **capable** of playing varsity hockey.
capable of 1. Ready and able to.
Even in his nineties, Bob Hope was still **capable of** entertaining an audience.
2. Having the qualities necessary for.
Although she's only fourteen, Samantha is **capable of** babysitting two small children.

congratulate
kən gra´ chə lāt

v. To express pleasure for a person's success or good fortune.
Allow me to **congratulate** you on your victory.
congratulations (kən gra chə lā´ shəns) *n. pl.* Good wishes.
Our class made Zel a card that said, "**Congratulations** on winning the 10k race!"

despise
di spīz´

v. To scorn and dislike strongly; to consider unworthy of respect.
The French nobles **despised** the peasants, whom they considered lacking in refinement.

dispute
di spyo͞ot´

n. A strong difference of opinion; an argument.
The feuding neighbors were unable to settle their **dispute** and finally took it to court.
v. To question the truth or value of.
When her parents **disputed** the value of her new bike, Rona produced an article in *Cycling* that praised it.

eventual
i ven´ cho͞o əl

adj. Coming at a later time; happening as a result of.
Years of practice led to his **eventual** success as a Wimbledon tennis champion.

helm
helm

n. 1. The wheel or tiller used to steer a boat.
The skipper said I could take the **helm** since the sea was calm.
2. A position of control.
With a new president at the **helm**, there is a strong likelihood that the company will grow.

humiliate
hyo͞o mi´ lē āt

v. To treat in a way that takes away a person's pride or self respect.
His fellow workers **humiliated** Hans Christian Andersen because he seemed so strange.
humiliation (hyo͞o mi´ lē ā´ shən) *n.* The act of humiliating or the state of being humiliated.
The emperor in the story could not hide his **humiliation** at the way the two "tailors" had tricked him.

implore
im plôr´

v. To plead with or beg for with much feeling.
I **implored** my parents to let me go with them.

insert
in surt´

v. To put in.
"Please **insert** fifty-five cents," said the voice on the phone.
n. (in´ surt) An extra piece sewn or put in place.
My new shirt has a lace **insert** at the neck.

outrage
out´ rāj

n. 1. Anger caused by injury or insult.
The decision to close the school caused **outrage** among the parents.
2. Anything that causes resentment or anger; a wicked or brutal act or remark.
"Capital punishment is an **outrage** and should be banned!" she shouted.
v. To fill with anger or resentment.
The way some people allow their dogs to run without a leash **outrages** me.

pierce
pirs

v. 1. To pass or break through.
A beam of light suddenly **pierced** the darkness.
2. To make a hole through.
The needle **pierced** the thick fabric easily.
piercing   *adj.* Very loud and shrill.
The **piercing** cries of the seagulls woke me up.

quiver
kwi´ vər

v. To shake with small, rapid movements; to tremble.
The child's lip **quivered** as if he were about to cry.
n. 1. A trembling.
There was a **quiver** in her voice as Mira told us about the accident.
2. A case for holding arrows.
Each archer was equipped with a bow and a **quiver** full of arrows.

release
ri lēs´

v. 1. To let go; to free.
The pigeons flew away as soon as I **released** them from their cages.
2. To make known.
A copy of the governor's speech was **released** to reporters at noon.
n. 1. A setting free.
Four years after his **release** from prison, Nelson Mandela was sworn in as South Africa's first black president.
2. A making known.
The publicity committee hurried to get out the press **release** so people would know about the play.

sullen
su´ lən

adj. Silent from anger or hurt.
Tom grew from a **sullen** teenager into a friendly and outgoing young man.

20A Finding Meanings

Choose two phrases to form a sentence that correctly uses a word from Word List 20. Write each sentence in the space provided.

1. (a) A quiver is   (c) an extra piece put into place.
   (b) A release is   (d) a case for arrows.

2. (a) A capable person is one who   (c) An outraged person is one
   (b) whose self-respect has been lost.   (d) is able to do things well.

3. (a) a rapid shaking movement.   (c) A quiver is
   (b) An arrest is   (d) a putting off until later.

4. (a) to deny that it is true.   (c) to make it known.
   (b) To insert a story is   (d) To release a story is

5. (a) An arrest is   (c) a stopping by an officer of the law
   (b) A dispute is   (d) a changing of one's mind.

6. (a) To humiliate someone is to   (c) make that person very angry.
   (b) plead with that person.   (d) To implore someone is to

7. (a) a sudden stop.   (c) A dispute is
   (b) an argument.   (d) A helm is

8. (a) is silently angry.   (c) A sullen person is one who
   (b) thinks fondly of the past.   (d) A humiliated person is one who

9. (a) to shock and anger that person.   (c) To despise someone is
   (b) to think highly of that person.   (d) To outrage someone is

10. (a) something that is removed.   (c) an extra piece put in place.
    (b) An insert is   (d) A helm is

20B Just the Right Word

Improve each of the following sentences by crossing out the bold phrase and replacing it with a word (or a form of the word) from Word List 20.

1. Her high soprano voice suddenly ~~broke through~~ *sullen* the silence of the auditorium.

2. They'll come around to your way of thinking ~~sooner or later.~~ *eventually*

3. Jeff was almost in tears as he ~~begged and pleaded with~~ *implored* me to help him with his math homework.

4. Unlike her cheerful sister, Noa had a ~~dark and gloomy~~ nature.

5. Six quarters must be ~~put into the slot~~ *inserted* before the washing machine will start.

6. I ~~questioned the correctness of~~ *dispute* the price I was charged because the sign said "Everything Half-Price."

7. Mr. Singh gave the carpenters his ~~good wishes~~ *congratulations* on a remodeling job well done.

8. My ~~loss of pride in what I was doing~~ *humiliation* was so great when the audience didn't even applaud that I rushed off the stage.

9. Nan and Johanna took turns at the ~~wheel used to steer the boat~~ *helm* on their tour of the islands.

10. Annabel will do a good job building the new bathroom because she is so ~~skilled and able~~ *capable*.

11. I ~~have a strong dislike for~~ *despise* those who are cruel to animals.

20C Applying Meanings

Circle the letter of each correct answer to the questions below. A question may have more than one correct answer.

arrest
capable
congratulate
despise
dispute
eventual
helm
humiliate
implore
insert
outrage
pierce
quiver
release
sullen

1. Which of the following might be **congratulated**?
   (a) a winner
   (b) a bride and groom
   (c) a victim
   (d) an intruder

2. Which of the following could be **released**?
   (a) a statement to the press
   (b) a prisoner
   (c) a caged animal
   (d) a door catch

3. Which of the following happens **eventually**?
   (a) you are born
   (b) you die
   (c) winter comes to an end
   (d) the football season begins

4. Which of the following has a **helm**?
   (a) a racing car
   (b) a canoe
   (c) a ship
   (d) a fortress

5. Which of the following might be **humiliating**?

    (a) being routed in a contest   (c) being hailed as a hero

    (b) showing courage   (d) being jeered at

6. Which of the following would be an **outrage**?

    (a) jailing an innocent person   (c) banning free speech

    (b) discovering a cure for a disease   (d) consoling a person who is sad

7. Which of the following can be **pierced**?

    (a) the skin   (c) the voice

    (b) the ears   (d) fog

8. Which of the following would we want **arrested**?

    (a) a lawbreaker   (c) the spread of a disease

    (b) the victim of a crime   (d) a pessimist

20D Word Study

Look at each group of four words below. If you think two of the words in a group are synonyms, circle them and write *S* in the space next to the words. If you think two of the words in a group are antonyms, circle them and write *A* in the space next to the words.

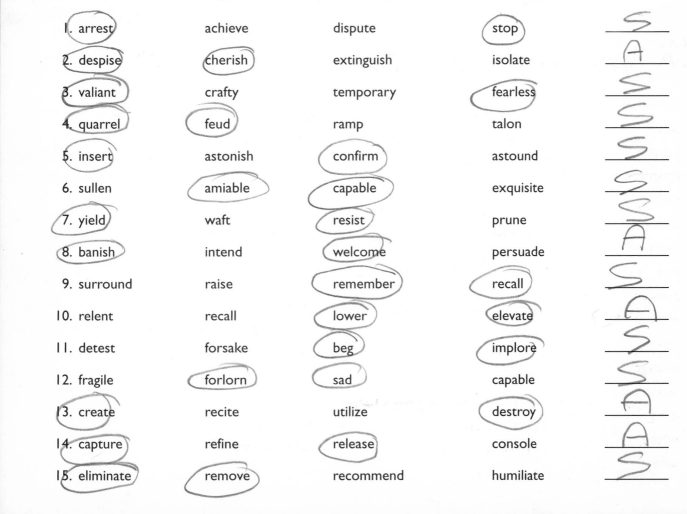

1. arrest	achieve	dispute	stop	S
2. despise	cherish	extinguish	isolate	A
3. valiant	crafty	temporary	fearless	S
4. quarrel	feud	ramp	talon	S
5. insert	astonish	confirm	astound	S
6. sullen	amiable	capable	exquisite	S
7. yield	waft	resist	prune	A
8. banish	intend	welcome	persuade	A
9. surround	raise	remember	recall	S
10. relent	recall	lower	elevate	A
11. detest	forsake	beg	implore	S
12. fragile	forlorn	sad	capable	S
13. create	recite	utilize	destroy	A
14. capture	refine	release	console	A
15. eliminate	remove	recommend	humiliate	S

Read the passage below; then complete the exercise that follows.

The Story of William Tell

In the town of Altdorf, Switzerland, stands a famous statue of William Tell, his son at his side, his crossbow slung over his shoulder. Although historians **dispute** William Tell's existence, and there is no evidence that he was a real person, Tell is a national hero to the Swiss people. He is a symbol of political and individual freedom.

Seven hundred years ago, the Swiss people were ruled by Austria. The governor of Switzerland was an Austrian named Gessler who **despised** the Swiss people and did not consider them **capable** of ruling themselves. One day, in order to **humiliate** them, he put his cap on a pole and ordered everyone in the town of Altdorf who passed by to bow before it. The Swiss people regarded the cap as a symbol of Austrian rule, and they detested it. However, the people of Altdorf had no choice, and they **sullenly** obeyed the order.

William Tell, a peasant from a nearby Swiss village, happened to be visiting Altdorf with his young son. Tell was famous for his skill as a boatman and was equally expert with the crossbow. He was also a proud man, and the people of the village watched as he approached the cap. Would he bow his head before it? No one was surprised to see him walk past the cap with his head held high. The Austrian guards **arrested** him for his "crime" and took him before the governor.

Gessler had heard of William Tell's remarkable skill with the crossbow, and it amused him to give his prisoner a choice: either go to prison or win freedom by shooting an apple from the top of his son's head at a hundred paces. Tell did not hesitate. After pacing out the distance, he removed two arrows from his **quiver**. He **inserted** the first one in the groove of his crossbow; the second arrow he tucked in his belt. He wound the spring of the crossbow and took careful aim. There was a tense silence as those watching waited for him to **release** the arrow. When he did so, it flashed through the air, splitting the apple cleanly in two. The boy was unharmed. After **congratulating** William Tell for demonstrating such skill, Gessler asked what the second arrow was for.

William Tell looked him in the eye and said, "If the first arrow had hurt my son, the second would have **pierced** your heart." Gessler was **outraged** by this reply and ordered Tell locked up for the rest of his life. But the boat that was carrying him across the lake to prison ran into a storm. The frightened crew knew that William Tell was a skilled boatman. They untied him and **implored** him to take over. Tell seized the **helm**. While the crew cowered below, he steered the boat toward the rocky shore. At the last moment he leaped ashore and escaped.

Once free, he lay in wait at a place where he knew Gessler would pass. When the governor did so, the arrow from William Tell's bow found its mark. Gessler died instantly. The news of William Tell's deed spread quickly and made him a hero to the Swiss people. It helped to unite them in their struggle and **eventually** led to their freedom from Austrian rule.

arrest

capable

congratulate

despise

dispute

eventual

helm

humiliate

implore

insert

outrage

pierce

quiver

release

sullen

Answer each of the following questions in the form of a sentence. If a question does not contain a vocabulary word from this lesson's word list, use one in your answer. Use each word only once. Questions and answers will then contain all fifteen words (or forms of the words).

1. Do you think William Tell's **arrest** was unjust?

2. How did the people of Altdorf show their feelings when told to bow before the cap?

3. Why was it **humiliating** for the Swiss to bow before Gessler's cap?

4. What does it mean to say that historians **dispute** the existence of William Tell?

5. What were Gessler's feelings toward the Swiss people?

6. Why did Gessler order William Tell to jail?

7. Why did Gessler think that Austria had a right to rule the Swiss people?

8. Why was everyone silent as they watched William Tell?

9. What did William Tell do with the two arrows?

10. What is the meaning of **quiver** as it is used in the passage?

11. What did William Tell intend to do with the second arrow?

12. How did Gessler react when the arrow split the apple in two?

13. Where was the crew while William Tell was at the **helm**?

14. How can we tell that the crew could not handle the boat?

15. Did Gessler's death have an immediate result?

FUN & FASCINATING FACTS

To **humiliate** someone is to make that person look weak or foolish in the eyes of others. The word comes from the Latin *humilis*, which means "low." This Latin word in turn comes from an older Latin word, *humus*, which means "earth" or "dirt." To *humiliate* someone is to treat that person "like dirt." Incidentally, *humus* is the English word for the decayed vegetable matter that enriches soil.

Humble (Word List 14) comes from the same Latin root. Someone of *humble* birth occupies a *low* position in society. To *humble* oneself is to *lower* oneself in the eyes of others.

There is another noun formed from *humiliate*, in addition to *humiliation*. It is related in meaning, but with an important difference. *Humility* is the state of being humble. It is considered by many to be a desirable state, the opposite of being boastful or vain.

Humiliation suggests being disgraced, having one's pride taken away.

If you weep while **imploring** a person to do something, your pleading might have a better chance of succeeding. At least, that is what the word suggests. It comes from the Latin *plorare*, which means "to cry out" or "to weep."

A **sullen** person is likely to shun the company of others or to be shunned by them. In either event, such a person is likely to be left alone. This should come as no surprise since the word comes from the Latin *solus*, which means "alone." For a number of other words formed from this Latin root see Lesson 13.

Review for Lessons 17–20

Crossword Puzzle Solve the crossword puzzle below by studying the clues and filling in the answer boxes. Clues followed by a number are definitions of words in Lessons 17 through 20. The number gives the word list in which the answer to the clue appears.

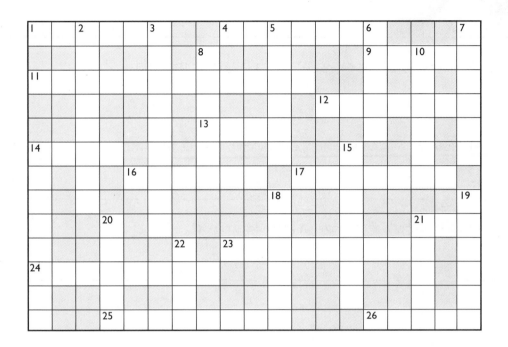

Clues Across

1. To go with, to guide or protect (17)
4. To think well of (17)
9. Opposite of *higher*
11. To express pleasure for a person's success (20)
12. To lift up; to make higher (19)
13. Of great size; enormous (18)
14. A long, bitter quarrel (18)
16. To make a hole through (20)
17. A person who makes a living from the soil (18)
21. You write with this
23. To take away the pride or self-respect of (20)
24. To fill with delight (19)
25. To warn someone that you might harm them (18)
26. Country in North Africa whose capital is Cairo

Clues Down

2. To end; to finish (17)
3. A custom handed down over time (19)
5. Used to make French fries
6. A person who is older (17)
7. To stop the movement or progress of (20)
8. A case for holding arrows (20)
10. Used to fight with
14. A building strong enough to be used for defense (18)
15. Something that gets in the way (18)
18. To send for (17)
19. An extra piece sewn or put in place (20)
20. To deserve (17)
21. Of little importance (18)
22. A tooth _____ or stomach _____